Gravitational Mystery Spots
of the United States

Explained Using the
Theory of Multidimensional Reality

By

Douglas B. Vogt

Vector Associates

BELLEVUE, WASHINGTON
1996

Published by Vector Associates
POB 40135, Bellevue Washington 98015
sales@vectorpub.com
(425) 643-1131; Fax: (240) 384-7297

Library of Congress Cataloging-in-Publication Data

Vogt, Douglas B., 1947–
   Gravitational mystery spots of the United States: explained using the theory of multidimensional reality / by Douglas B. Vogt
   p. cm.
   ISBN 0-930808-04-5 (alk. Paper)
   1. Gravity anomalies—United States—Measurement.
QB337.5.U5V64   1996
526' .7' 0979—dc21   96-39110   CIP

Printed in the United States of America

Vector Associates
P.O. Box 40135
Bellevue, WA 98015
Fax: (425) 643-1131
E-mail: sales@vectorpub.com

Gravitational Mystery Spots of the United States

ISBN 0-930808-04-5

$12.95 US

$14.95 Canadian

Dedication

To my wife Susan and my Son David.

ACKNOWLEDGMENTS

The author is grateful for the help he received from Mr. Vic Ardelean who supplied his motor home to travel to the Santa Cruz Mystery Spot in Santa Cruz CA, the Confusion Hill in Piercy CA, and Magnetic Hill in Petaluma, CA. He also helped me perform the experiments there. I also want to thank him for some editing and suggestions he offered. I would like to thank my wife, Susan, for doing the proofreading and some editing of this book.

I would like to thank Mr. Terry Cooper; manager and son of the owner of the Oregon Vortex for letting me do the experiments on June 2nd and 9th and for the information he shared with me.

I would like to thank Mr. Bruce Willis, owner of Confusion Hill, for letting me do the experiments there.

I would like to thank Bernard Ingram, the manager of the Santa Cruz Mystery Spot for letting me do the experiments there and to his staff for sharing miscellaneous information with me.

Excerpts of the mythology sections were taken from my previously published book, Reality Revealed; The Theory of Multidimensional Reality ©1977.

Third Party Trademarks:
Oregon Vortex® is a registered trademark.

Table of Contents

*J*ntroduction

An anomaly is something that deviates from the normal reality and is outside a scientific explanation. A phenomenon is a fact or event that exists in time and space that defies accepted scientific explanation. These phenomena are really a special portal in the fabric of our reality that let us perceive what existence truly is. We try to understand what we see and sense by applying the scientific philosophies we have been taught. For the past fifty years our scientific instruments have outstripped our ability to understand what they are measuring, detecting, and "seeing". Over the past 100 years science has changed from a classical Newtonian model of the universe to a relativistic Einsteinian approach to finally a quantum mechanical approach with subatomic particles and quarks making up matter. All of these approaches are based on a matter-oriented theory of existence, the idea that matter is the dominant thing in the universe, that the interaction of all forms of matter, from molecules to particles, cause and explain the world we live in. Over the past forty years the list of unexplained phenomena have grown to a substantial number in all the major fields of science. The question is: When will their house of cards come crashing down around their square caps, forcing a new philosophy of science to emerge?

In the 1968 motion picture, *Planet of the Apes*, we see man returning to a future earth. The apes have evolved and man has devolved. If viewers of the movie thought that evolution was the theme of the movie, they missed the most important point. The film was showing how ignorance is institutionalized in politics, religion, and in higher education. The elders of the apes knew there was something past the "forbidden zone." They knew that there was a more advanced civilization before theirs and it was not descended from them. To keep control of the masses, certain thought processes had to be repressed.

Mankind's institutions have been just as kind to us as apekind's institutions were to them. Only certain kinds of thinking or non-thinking are rewarded in our world. There is no financial reward in thinking creatively. There are financial rewards for thinking "properly." "Properly" is the way we have been taught to accept.

So the question I pose to you is: Why did I write a book about some gravitational anomalies on the west coast of North America and why are they important? Most of them are tourist oddities operated by small families attracting dozens of tourists daily. All claim the "shrink and grow" phenomenon and all have a crocked two room shack built on them. Critics would say: So what is so special about an optical illusion? The definition of an illusion is: a misleading image presented to the vision. The answer is that these are not illusions and time changes dynamically inside these gravitational vortex anomalies. Their importance is they prove that the traditional explanation for gravity (the general theory of relativity) is wrong!

What is wrong with the "accepted" philosophy of science is the foundation of our scientific theories of existence are based on a matter-oriented theory of existence. Matter is the dominant thing in the universe. I believe this is the fundamental error our society has made. It is leading to a dead-end in scientific thought. The only other alternative for explaining the workings of the universe is that "information" is the dominant force in the universe. The information, from another dimension, creates the matter world in which we exist.

My first philosophy of science book was *Reality Revealed: The Theory of Multidimensional Reality* written in 1977. As far as I know, it was the first time in history anyone had presented an information theory of existence and applied it to many of the phenomena in our universe, including what causes the ice ages, polar reversals, mass extinction's, creation of new species, great flood, and other events all happening at the same time geologically.

With this book I wanted to choose a narrowly focused phenomena that the average person could go see for themselves, experience, test, and photograph. After that they could read my explanation using the Theory of Multidimensional Reality and decide for themselves.

I investigated four sites during the week of June 1 to June 9th 1996. They were the Oregon Vortex in Gold Hill Oregon, Magnetic Hill east of Rohnert Park, California, the Santa Cruz Mystery Spot in Santa Cruz, California, and Confusion Hill in

Piercy, California. We were at each location for one day except for the Oregon Vortex, where I stayed there for an extra day. Chapter 1 covers the scope of the experiment and what I was looking for. Chapters 2 through 5 cover the results from each location. Chapter 6 goes into an in-depth explanation of the Theory of Multidimensional Reality that explains the phenomena observed. In Chapter 7 I explain what mechanism is causing these strange phenomena.

The first thing that should be done is to explain what are the traditional explanations of gravity and what are some of the important equations so that you can identify for yourself which theory makes sense and which doesn't.

Traditional Explanation of Gravity

The classical definition of gravity, as presented by Sir Isaac Newton, is that it is proportional to the mass of an object or planet and inversely proportional to the square of the distance from the center of the two objects or planets. Newton presents two propositions in the *Law of Universal Gravitation*.

1. *There is a power of gravity pertaining to all bodies, proportional to the several quantities of matter which they contain.*
2. *The force of gravity towards the several equal particles of any body is inversely as the square of the distance of places from the particles.*

The law is expressed by this equation $F = Gm_1m_2/d^2$, where m_1 and m_2 are any two masses, d is the distance between the two objects, F is the force of gravity between the two objects, and G is the universal constant (6.670×10^{-8} dyne cm^2 gm^{-2}).

In the early part of the twentieth century (1916) Albert Einstein developed his General Theory of Relativity which incorporates his theories on gravitation. He assumed that gravity is a physical effect produced by the curvature of a four-dimensional space-time, with the fourth dimension being time. Where Newton had four index tensors or vectors to describe the curvature of space-time, Einstein uses ten tensors of Riemannian's space-time geometry.

The important thing to remember is with both approaches gravity is due to mass. Height or size is directly proportional to the gravitational field the object is in. With the General Theory of Relativity, time slows down and objects get smaller when they are in the proximity of a strong gravitational field. The shrink and grow phenomenon found at all three gravitational vortexes have been explained away by saying that there is some large meteor or metal mass buried down below. All three attractions have reported greater than a 7% size change in their vortexes. Such a size change would represent a mass of such great density or size that it is implausible such a body exists in the geological areas where these attractions are situated. I will show, using the results of the experiments that the traditional theories of existence do not explain what gravity truly is, and what is going on in these gravitational vortexes.

The scope of this book is not to demonstrate the field equations of the General Theory of Relativity or to try to calculate the size and density of a mass necessary to create the observed effect. I just want the reader to understand that traditional science philosophy cannot explain the observed phenomena at these locations and if they are genuine, then academia, society, and most importantly—you must decide: Do the traditional philosophies of existence fall or do we continue to hide and ignore these very special phenomena? If society chooses the latter, they are sticking their heads in the dirt, as man did in the Dark Ages thinking that the flat earth was the center of the universe.

Gravitational Vortex Anomalies of the United States

Listed below are all the gravitational anomalies we know of in the United States. I have tested only the four mentioned above. I have not tested the others, therefore, I cannot authenticate their genuineness. Their distribution throughout the United States will enable readers to travel to these sites and do their own testing and make up their own mind. Some of these locations are not commercial attractions. Some are just a stretch of road such as Magnetic Hill, California. Next to these locations I have place an asterisk (*). Chapter 1 covers the experiments, procedures, and equipment, so you can duplicate the same experiments and see if you get the same results.

Arizona
Rose Point*, *Sedona, Arizona*

California

The Mystery Spot, *465 Mystory Spot Rd., Santa Cruz, California 95063*
(408) 423-8897
Has a two room cabin, has shrink and grow phenomenon, on the side of a hill.
Discovered 1940, 150' in diameter.

Confusion Hill, *75001 North Hwy 101, Piercy, California 95587*
(707) 925-6456
Has a two room cabin, has shrink and grow phenomenon, on the side of a hill.
Discovered 1949, 100' in diameter.

Gravity Grade*, *Mt. Baldy, Pomona, California*

Magnetic Hill*, *Lichau Rd, Petaluma, California*
Automobiles appear to roll up the hill. 300' long.

Florida

Spook Hill* (a stretch of road), *N. Wales Drive, Lake Wales, Florida*
Automobiles appear to roll up the hill.

The Mystery Spot, *St. Augustine, Florida*

Michigan

Mystery Hill, *7611 US Hwy 12, Irish Hill, Michigan 49265*
(517) 467-2517
Has a two room cabin, claims shrink and grow phenomenon, on the side of a hill.

The Mystery Spot, *150 Martin Lake Rd., St. Ignace, Michigan 49781*
(906) 643-8322
Has a two room cabin, claims shrink and grow phenomenon, on the side of a hill.   Discovered 1953, 300' in diameter.

North Carolina

Mystery Hill, *129 Mystery Hill Ln., Blowing Rock, NC 28605*
(704) 264-2792
Has a two room cabin, claims shrink and grow phenomenon, on side of a hill.
Discovered 1950.

Ohio

Mystery Hill, *8232 Harbor Blvd., Marblehead, Ohio 43440*
(419) 798-5230
Has a cabin, claims shrink and grow phenomenon, on side of a hill.

Oregon

The Oregon Vortex, *4303 Sardine Creek Rd., Gold Hill, Oregon
97525* (541) 855-1543
Has a two room cabin, has shrink and grow phenomenon,
on side of a hill.
Discovered 1935, 165' in diameter.
Uncanny Canyon*, *Crater Lake, Oregon;* Exact location unknown.
Unnamed area, *located near Coquille, Oregon;* Exact location un-
known.

South Dakota

The Cosmos of the Blackhills, *24040 Cosmos Road, Rapid City,
SD 57702*
(605) 343-9802
Has a two room cabin, claims shrink and grow phenomenon,
on side of a hill.
Discovered 1952.

New Brunswick, Canada

Magnetic Hill*, *Trans Canada Hwy 2 (near Mountain Rd.), Moncton,
New Brunswick, E1C 5B2*
(506) 384-2350
Automobiles appear to roll up the hill. Discovered 1933.

Tennessee

Mystery Hill, *Dudley Creek Rd. and US 441, Gatlinburg, Tennessee,*
Attraction not open.

Wisconsin

The Wonder Spot, *Hwy 12 (Exit 92), Lake Delton, Wisconsin 53940*
(608) 254-4224
Has a two room cabin, on side of a hill.
Discovered 1948. 55' in diameter.

Wyoming

The Teton Mystery, *S. Hwy 89, Box 1412, Jackson, Wyoming 83001*
(307) 733-4285
Has a cabin, claims shrink and grow phenomenon, on the
side of a hill.
Discovered 1939. Smaller then 100' in diameter.

Chapter 1

The Test Procedures
and the Search

The Oregon Vortex® and the Santa Cruz Mystery Spot were familiar to me because of previous visits to them five and ten years earlier. I knew what both attractions claimed and I wanted to set up some experiments that would test the phenomena and quantify the results. The attractions claimed the following phenomena:

1. Objects and people would shrink and grow depending on where the individuals stood in relation to the center of the gravitational anomaly. That means a person or object who was closer to the center of the anomaly would be shorter than the object further away or outside the area.
2. A dead weight hanging freely from above would be harder to push towards the center of the anomaly than away from it.
3. The percentage of the shrink and grow phenomenon would vary over time. The change in height would vary from one day to the next and sometimes during the same day.
4. Standing objects would tend to lean into the center of the anomaly.
5. Compasses did not work properly within the anomaly.
6. The Oregon Vortex® claimed the anomaly was acting like it was a vortex flowing or moving.
7. Some people would get headaches in the anomaly.
8. Some people would have relief of pain in the vortex.
9. Some trees would grow with a noticeable counter-clockwise twist or some branches would grow curved following the vortex lines of "force".

I had been to the Oregon Vortex® five years before and had

performed some time tests with a 25 MHz crystal oscillator. The results obtained were very encouraging and warranted a more in-depth study.

There were problems with the three attractions that were to be tested. The Oregon Vortex® would let me test the time shift but only from one direction. I would like to have measured the vortex from other directions. I did learn from the other two sites that it really did not matter but it would be better conformation where the center was and if the gravitational field was even throughout the vortex. The staff at the Oregon Vortex® was the most knowledgeable about the anomaly and had the best literature describing the phenomena.

The Santa Cruz Mystery Spot was easy to access from the street side but was very difficult from the back hillside of the attraction. We had to approach the anomaly from both sides, so we could locate the center of the vortex. Staffers were not really sure as to the location of the center.

The Confusion Hill attraction had no tour guides and it was on the side of a fairly steep hill. There was very little level ground that we could take the shrink and grow photographs. They also did not know the locationwhere the center.

Time Constraints for the Experiments

We could not stay longer than one to two days at each site because of our own time constraints. The attractions could not have us stretching the cables for long periods of time. There was some danger that a visitor could trip and fall over the cables or other equipment. I did not want to interfere with them demonstrating and showing the attractions to paying tourists. Hourly and daily fluctuations in frequency were noticed. After these experiments were over I came to believe it is important these sites be tested over long periods of time such as one month.

Shrink and Grow Phenomenon

The one phenomenon that defines these special gravitational anomalies is the observation that objects and people get smaller, as they get closer to the center. This effect is reminiscent of the General Theory of Relativity. As objects get closer to a large mass, its gravitational field warps time and the size of objects in its vicinity. It is because of the General Theory of Relativity that scientists have assumed there is a meteor or other large massive metal object buried under these sites. The problem with this assumption is the Oregon and Santa Cruz sites are located in areas of sediment probably no older then 36,000 years and all three locations have no evidence of iron or other heavy metals in their regions. Also, the size or density of a meteor would have to be huge to create the size and time changes observed in all three sites and this is just not the case because the size of the anomalies are not greater then 165 feet. In fact if it was a meteor we would be seeing a creater as larke as the one in Arizona.

All the attractions tested had two room wooden shacks built on them. The Oregon Vortex® was the first and oldest attraction. The other two attractions were copies of the Oregon site. Looking at the sales brochures of the other gravitational anomalies around the country they all seemed to be built based on the Oregon model. The shacks are built leaning on the side of hills. They are built to confuse the eye and create an optical illusion. I now know the shacks of these sites, really confuse the issue of the gravitational anomaly. It would be better if the site was bulldozed level and then a building was put on it.

All three attractions had photos of the shrink and grow phenomenon, but the photos were useless because the camera was not placed perpendicular at the midpoint between the two sub-

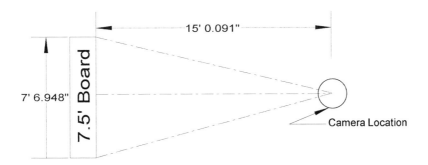

Figure 1: layout of the measuring board and camera tripod.

jects. Usually the camera was placed on the side where the larger image was (farther away from the center of the anomaly). The result was the picture accentuated the effect. Sometimes the camera was moved after the first picture and moved back, which would also accentuate the shrink and grow phenomenon. To avoid this a 7'6" long board was used as a platform with the midpoint marked (Figure 1). Two 6'3" white polls are attached for reference heights. Three wires were precut to make sure the camera and tripod were placed 15' from the center of the board. When the space at the site did not permit 15', the camera tripod was measured independently to make sure placement was midpoint and level.

Time Shifts

The General Theory of Relativity calls for time to slow down as objects approach a large gravitational mass. Time slows down on clocks placed near a black hole. The clock itself would also get much smaller. This is similar to the Special Theory of Relativity that holds that time slows down and objects get smaller as they approach the speed of light.

My experimental approach was that if there was a time shift associated with the size change, then it would rule out any possibility of optical illusions or trickery. To measure any time shifts I used a 25 MHz freely oscillating crystal powered by a 9 volt battery. I used only Eveready® Energizers® because they started with 9.4 volts and their discharge rate was consistent. The crystals' frequency output averaged 24,997,980 over eight hours, plus or minus 6 hertz. Table 1 plots the frequency output, in normal time and space, over eight hours. Table 2 shows a more detailed graph covering the first hour and ten minutes. The chart only displays the last four numbers of the frequency. The frequency output was fairly stable for such a simple circuit. It was a simple circuit with no voltage regulating or frequency compensating circuitry. As long as the voltage was above 6 voltage, the crystal operated within the frequency range. I tested and plotted the crystal oscillator in Bellevue, Washington, which I considered "normal" space and time. The 35 MHz frequency counter was able to display single hertz or cycles. This was important because I wanted to measure the slightest change in time. The crystal was connected to the frequency counter by a 113' 58 W coax or a 200' coax. I was also able to connect the two cables together if extra length was needed. The frequency counter was powered by both line voltage as well as a 12-volt 31 amp gel cell battery. The frequency counter was tested with both power sources and there was virtually no difference in output readings or performance.

The time measurements used in the experiment are the hours and minutes from when the 9-volt battery was put into the frequency generating crystal source (the crystal). The procedure was the same for all the locations. First the

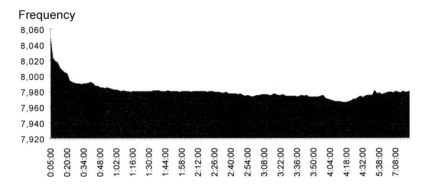

Table 1: The frequency output, in normal time and space, over eight hours.

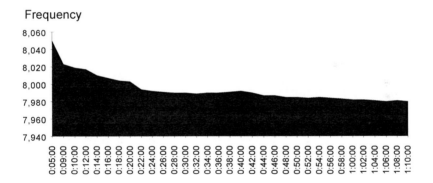

Table 2: The frequency output, in normal time and space, over 90 minutes.

new 9-volt battery was loaded into the crystal source. The frequency counter was turned on and both were left for over 30 minutes so they would both reach ambient temperature and the frequency would stabilize. Next, the crystal was brought into the anomaly to see where the lowest or highest frequency was indicated so the center could be located. I received some strange frequency readings from all three locations, when we first brought the crystal into the anomaly. I discuss this in-depth in Chapter 7.

Five years ago I did some time experiments with the same crystal and frequency counter at the Oregon Vortex®. The observation then was the frequency would shift up. This time I observed frequencies shifting up and down. This will also be discussed in chapters dedicated to each gravitational anomaly and Chapter 7 (The Conclusion). I also discovered that the number of people entering these anomalies also affected the frequency.

Force Moving a Dead Weight

All three attractions had iron weights hanging from the ceiling in the wooden shacks. Because all of the shacks were built crooked or were now crooked, it made it hard to measure the force because we didn't have a flat floor to rest the test equipment on. At the Oregon Vortex® I used my own weight suspension system and used it outside on level ground. At Confusion Hill and the Mystery Spot we hung our 25 lb. weight from the ceiling and measured the force with our equipment. We were able to get consistent results from all three locations. We did these experiments after we located the center of the vortex and had done most of our frequency or time tests.

Proof of the Shrink and Grow Phenomenon

The big problem was making sure the camera and tripod were set up equidistant between both individuals and perpendicular to the board they stood on. The center of the anomaly had to be located so the subjects would be in-line with the center. There were problems at the Mystery Spot because the area next to the two-room cabin was not that level and it was not a full 15' from our board. At Confusion Hill there was a noticeable shrink and grow phenomenon, but the area was not wide enough to place the 7.6' board, so we had to use their platform. The tripod had to be placed inside the shack because of a lack of room.

Leaning into the Center of the Vortex

All attractions claimed that people standing inside the vortex would appear to lean towards the center. We tested this claim by dropping a plum line and photographing one of us standing next to it. For this experiment it was important to first locate the center of the vortex, so we knew where we to stand.

The Compass Experiments

Some places have claimed that a compass does not work properly in the anomaly. We used two compasses to locate true north. We both noticed no problem with our compasses used for direction. To do this experiment properly, I should have had an electronic compass/direction finder but due to cost of such equipment it could not be used. We were told at the Mystery Spot in Santa Cruz that a German scientist had brought a magnetometer into the anomaly to measure magnetic fields. He recorded significant changes over very short distances within the vortex. These changes normally occur over many miles, so something unusual was recorded. It would be worthwhile for someone to do a mapping of these anomalies with a magnetometer to see if a grid pattern shows up which is what John Litster claimed at the Oregon Vortex. He used a dowsing rod to locate what he called terralines located 57" apart.

The Mystery Spot and the Oregon Vortex® both claimed that pilots notice compass changes many thousands of feet in the air.

Do Gravitational Anomalies Behave Like a Vortex?

The definition of a vortex is a mass of a fluid having a whirlpool or circular motion tending to form a cavity or vacuum in the center of the circle and to draw towards this cavity or vacuum bodies subject to its action. Mr. John Litster is the one who labeled the Oregon anomaly a vortex because he felt the forces within the anomaly were rotating around a center point. He observed people and objects leaning towards the center of the anomaly. He also observed the madrona trees, within the "vortex," would bend in the same direction. He interpreted the bending to the terralines causing the tree limb to bend, when they came in contact. All of the attractions demonstrate such tree limb bending, as well as trees that grow twisted like a corkscrew counter-clockwise.

The scope of my experiments were not to locate these terralines nor to measure any force movement within these anomalies. Since we observed such twisting of trees in all three locations, I will accept the idea that some sort of vortex action is occurring within the anomalies. Throughout this book I will interchangeably use vortex and anomaly as one and the same.

Unexpected Surprises

As with most experiments one gets surprises when they are performed in the field. I had made some assumptions as to what the frequency reading would be and the amount of shrink and grow that would be observed. When I performed the frequency test five years before I had observed the crystal frequency shifting up as it was placed closer to the center. What was observed was a surprise and further proved a large meteor buried a long time ago could not cause that anomaly. Chapters 2 through 5 covers what was measured and discovered at the four test locations. I encourage any person, with curiosity, to perform your own tests at these locations and see what you come up with.

Chapter 2
The Oregon Vortex®

The Oregon Vortex® is located at 4303 Sardine Creek Road in Gold Hill, Oregon. The operators say the shack (Figure 3 and 5) was an assay office and tool shed for a mining company. John Litster was the first researcher and owner of the attraction. The mining company must have closed down sometime before Litster started his investigations in 1914 but no date was given. They also say that over the years before Litster took it over, the shack had slid down the hill some 40′ but no date range was given for this miraculous event. It now rests next to a large tree. The attraction has

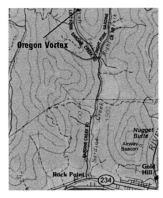

Figure 2: Location map of the Oregon Vortex®.

Figure 3: The shack at the Oregon Vortex® looking south. The center of the vortex is to the left of the building.

been open to the public since 1930, which makes it the oldest of all these type of attractions. I have examined the two room shack and I believe their cover story about the shack is untrue.[1] I think it is more likely that it was built crooked by Litster as a tourist attraction to accentuate the effects in the vortex.

John Litster did his research in the 1930s to early '50s. In his research notes he attempts to describe the phenomena by incorporating some unrelated scientific concepts used in the 1940s[2] He ultimately says this anomaly is like a vortex, because of its circular shape. He describe the structure by a series of "terralines" some 57 inches apart oriented to the four compus points and intersecting at 90°.[3] He also assumes the phenomenon is electromagnetic in origin. He describes the circular 165' area in question, expanding and contracting periodically.

The Start of the Experiment

The procedure for starting the experiment was the same for all of the sites tested. When I arrived, a new 9 volt battery was put into the crystal frequency source. This was done because from previous testing, in Bellevue Washington, it was realized there was a 25 to 30 minute warm-up period, after which the circuit reached its ambient operating temperature. The time was 11:32 AM June 2, 1996 when the battery was put in. The times listed in the experiment are duration time from the installation of the battery. It was 12:08 PM when the frequency counter, cable, and crystal were set up. I had the frequency counter turned on for about ten minutes before it was connected to the crystal. Both, I thought, were outside the vortex.

Five years before, I had located the center of the vortex, so I stretched out a 100' metal tape measure from the center going north to the frequency counter. The shorter cable is 113' long, so the frequency counter was about 112' from the center. If Litster was correct, the radius of the vortex should have been 82.5', plus a corona area he describes as being 27' wide, gives us a 109.5' radius to be completely out of the influence of the vortex. The reason I am going into a little more detailed description of the location of the equipment is because I got a big surprise when the counter started reading the frequency from the crystal. I placed the crystal at the 100' mark to start. What I noticed was the frequency was fluctuating wildly by several thousand hertz. My frequency counter and crystal had never done that, and at first I thought something had broken or come loose. I brought the crystal back to the frequency counter and waited a few minutes to see what was going to happen. The frequency swing started reducing. I also checked the equipment and found nothing wrong. I then disconnected the cable from the frequency counter when, much to my surprise, the counter was displaying from 10 to 500 hertz for a few minutes thereafter. I had never seen this before, so I assumed that a strong RF field coming from the vortex effected the counter. I decided to move the frequency counter much further away from the center, so the other 200' cable was connected. The frequency counter was now 170' away from the center. I reconnected the cable with the crystal and just waited to see if the counter would stabilize over time. At 1:17 PM the frequency counter stabilized and the first run of the experiment started.

After observing similar start-up frequency fluctuations at the Mystery Sport, Confusion Hill, and Magnetic Hill I realized that this was something special and was not a malfunction of the equipment. Because of this observation and another, I was prompted to test the Oregon Vortex® again on June 9. That visit confirmed a hunch I had developed while testing these anomalies (see Chapter 7).

Time Fluctuation Results

The frequency tests are really measuring time. That's why these tests are so important. If time is changing, then what we are seeing is not an optical illusion. Currently, there is no way that man knows how to alter time or make objects smaller so the element of trickery was eliminated. The first series of tests were done June of 1991. The results of all three runs were frequency shifted upwards as the crystal was placed near the center of the vortex.

Experiments of June 1991

The frequency counter was placed 110' away from the center. Only the 113' coax cable was used.

Experimental test run number 1 (Table 3) started at 1:00 PM. Measurement started at the 100' mark and proceeded toward the center. The frequency counter started at 24,998,078

Frequency

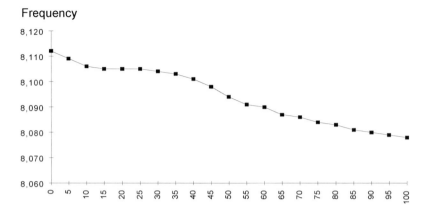

Table 3: Run number 1; measuring frequency from the 100′ mark into the center of the vortex using 113′ of cable. Start time: 1:00 PM. Duration of the experiment: 16 minutes.

Hz. The graphs only display the last four numbers (8,078 Hz.). The 9 volt battery was in the crystal source for 15 minutes before the experiment started. The adjusted frequency difference

Frequency

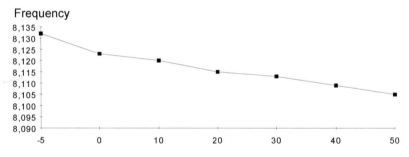

Table 4: Run number 2; measuring frequency from the 50′ mark into the center of the vortex using 113′ of cable. Start time: 1:25 PM. Duration of the experiment: 6 minutes.

from outside to inside was 34 hertz. The frequency inside was higher than outside.

The second run (Table 4) started at the 50′ mark, and then proceeded to the center, and then 5 feet beyond.

The third run (Table 5) started at the 100′ mark and proceeded only to the 50′ mark. This was done to help locate the edge of the anomaly.

The conclusion I came to, five years ago, was that frequency

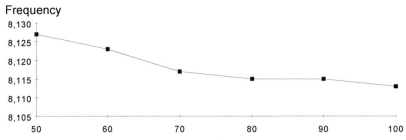

Table 5: Run number 3; measuring frequency from the 100′ mark to the 50′ mark of the vortex using 113′ of cable. Start time: 2:00 PM. Duration of the experiment: 5 minutes.

only shifted upwards towards the center of the anomaly and that time was affected. There did seem to be an edge to the vortex about 70′ from the center.

Experiments of June 2, 1996

The crystal was placed in the approximate center of the vortex at 1:17 PM and the frequency counter recorded a frequency of 24,997,934 hertz ±4 hertz. The graph displayed in Table 6 displays only the last 4 digits (7,934 Hz), because the changes observed were always less then 1,000 hertz (except for the start-

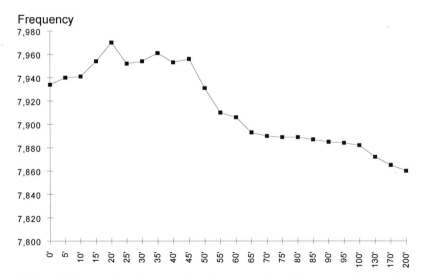

Table 6: Run number 1; measuring frequency from the center (approx.) to 200′ from the center. Start time: was 1:17 PM. Duration of the experiment: 47 minutes. Using Lorenz's transformation for time, this 110/24,997,970 of a second change represents a clock traveling at 552.6 miles per second!

up period).

Frequency was higher near the center of the anomaly than outside. There was a 110 hertz difference between inside and out. At the 65' mark it appeared the frequency stabilized. This may be the edge of the vortex but not the edge of all of its effect as Litster had noted there was a corona of a certain distance around the anomaly. The only problem is he does not explain how he determined it was a corona.

The second run (Table 7) measured from the frequency

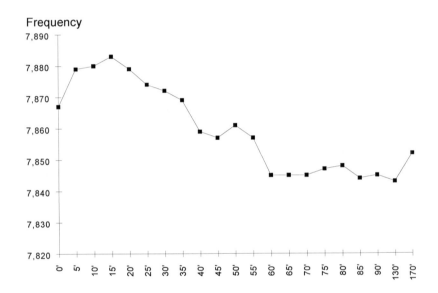

Table 7: Run number 2; measuring frequency from the frequency counter to the center of the vortex. Start time: 2:04 PM. Duration of the experiment: 33 minutes.

counter at 170' into the vortex. The frequency difference was 40 hertz.

A new battery was put into the crystal oscillator at 2:42 PM. After 22 minutes the third run (Table 8) was begun. The frequency difference between inside and out was 50 hertz. All three runs recorded frequencies higher in the center than outside.

I performed a fourth run (Table 9), but at the time I thought it was inclusive and confusing because the frequency started out at 24,997,889 Hz (3:36 PM) at the 100' mark. Then went down to 24,997,887 Hz at the center (3:47 PM). Then when I brought the crystal out again, the frequency dropped down at the 25′ mark, then proceeded back up to 24,997,884 Hz at the 100′ mark, which is 5 hertz from where it started from. Table 9 shows the puzzling result.

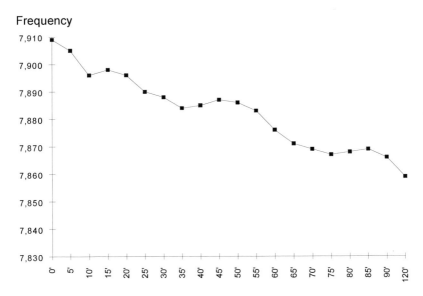

Frequency

Table 8: Run number 3; measuring frequency from the 115′ mark into the center of the vortex using 313′ of cable. Start time 3:04 PM. Duration of the experiment 22 minutes.

Remember, sometimes it is the unexpected surprise that gives you a deeper insight into what is going on. What I had recorded was the frequency changing, within the vortex, in front of my very eyes. Terry Cooper, manager of the Oregon Vortex®, told me that the shrink and grow effect will change from day-to-day, and sometimes during the day, they will notice a difference. For instance, they have two 7′ poles at the beginning of the tour. Some days, one pole will look 6″ shorter, the next day it will look 3″ shorter. When he told me this, on June 2, I thought that maybe the frequency was changing dynamically. It would not be easy determining frequency, unless readings were taken over long periods of time, and multiple runs were made so a pattern could be established.

Frequency

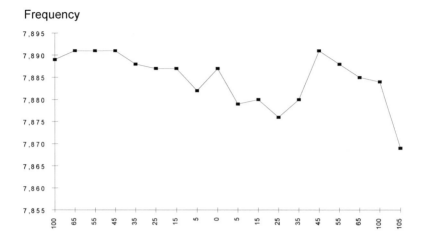

Table 9: Run number 4; measuring frequency from the 100' mark into the center of the vortex using 113' of cable. Start time: 3:36 PM. Duration of the experiment: 22 minutes.

Dynamic Change

After testing Confusion Hill and the Mystery Spot, the question was: were these gravitational anomalies dynamically changing over time? At both those locations I created a new test by leaving the crystal at one location, for a number of hours, and record the frequency fluctuation over time.

Experiments of June 9, 1996

On this visit I only wanted to check one thing. What was the frequency change over time, if the crystal was left at one location. The experiment started at 12:12 PM, June 9, 1996. The crystal was placed at the 15' mark and frequency was recorded every 2 minutes. Only the 113' cable was used and the frequency counter was 125' away from the center. It was left there for 93 minutes. For test purposes, I also placed the crystal outside the vortex some 240' away from the center to see if the frequency counter was recording frequency properly. The crystal was placed this distance after 48 minutes inside the vortex. It remained at 240' for about 10 minutes. During that time the frequency stabilized at 24,998,073 ±2 hertz. After the crystal was put back at the 15' mark it resumed the same frequency pattern it did before. While the crystal was located at the 15' mark, there was a variation in frequency output. Over the two-minute interval, the frequency variation ranged beyond what I was comfortable with. That is one of the reasons I placed the crystal at the 240' mark, to see if it was the equipment or was it recording something real. At this point, I concluded that it was something real. For some time the frequency variation was over 20 hertz. In Table 10 I have shown the high and low frequency recorded 15 seconds after the 2 minute mark.

Frequency

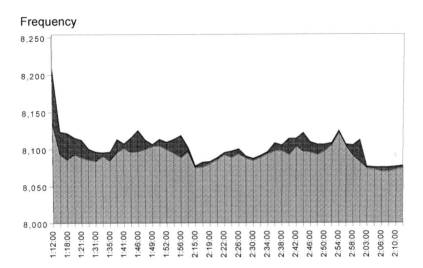

Table 10: Measuring frequency from the 15' mark from the center of the vortex using 113' of cable. At 2:02 elapse time, the crystal was taken to 240' away from the center. Start time: 3:36 PM. Duration of the experiment: 22 minutes.

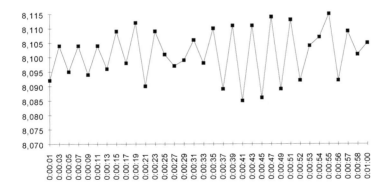

Table11: Measuring frequency from the 15' mark for one minute. Start time: 12:40 PM. Duration of the experiment: 1 minute.

During the middle of this experiment (12:40 PM), I decided to record the frequency output per second for one minute to see if a pattern would emerge. Table 11 shows a graph of the output frequencies for that minute. There looks like a pattern is present. I do not have a frequency counter that could record the output over a long period of time, but that would be a very enlightening experiment that should be done.

Force Moving a Dead Weight

I built a suspension device (Figure 4) that was put on a level area and placed in-line with the center of the vortex. This was in a west to east direction. Table 12 shows the force, in pounds, to move the 25 lb. weight 10" to 15" towards and away from the center of the anomaly. The scale used was a common kitchen scale that I had calibrated and found was good enough to show any force difference. The results clearly show it takes as much as 20% more force to push the weight 15 inches towards the center then away. The explanation for this phenomenon is in Chapter 7.

Figure 4: Weight suspension experiment showing the 25 lb. weight.

Inches	% Difference
10"	1.038
11"	1.059
12"	1.067
13"	1.125
14"	1.129
15"	1.202

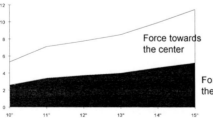

Force towards the center

Force away from the center

Table 12: Graph showing the force in pounds to move a 25 lb. weight 10" to 15"

Shrink and Grow Phenomenon

The main attractions of these tourist sites are the shrink and grow phenomenon. Usually two people will stand on opposite sides of a level plank or concrete slap. When they change positions, the observers, perpendicular to the subjects, see the change in heights. The problem with most of these exhibits is that they can be the product of an optical illusion, because of the crooked building with a sloping fence as a backdrop. The Oregon Vortex® has three platforms where people could see this phenomenon. I set up the tripod and camera at the cabin courtyard, which was level. Figure 5 and 6 shows a 5.4% shrink observed[4]. Figure 7 and 8 shows two subjects standing on a level, concrete slab near the gift shop and southwest of the center. The two poles are both 7' tall. There is a 5.8% shrink factor for the one standing to the right.[4] Both locations show a similar shrink and grow phenomenon.

In Litster's research notes he has two photos that show a

Figure 5: Author is standing to the right and farther away from the center of the anomaly.

9%+ shrink percentage north of the shack. The two men are standing on a plank running east and west. I had tested the same location (Figure 5 and 6) but came up with 5.4% shrink effect. One of the discrepancies in his notes is he says that this effect

Figure 6: Author is standing to the left and closer to the center of the anomaly. He gets 5.4% smaller over a distance of 7′.

Figure 7: Author is standing to the left and farther away from the center of the anomaly.

Figure 8: Author is standing to the right and closer to the center of the anomaly. He gets 5.8% smaller over a distance of 8'.

only occurs on a north-south alignment along one of these terralines and none on an east-west direction even though he shows, as well as I in Figures 5 and 6, it occurs on an east-west alignment.[5] My experiment clearly shows the shrink and grow phenomenon is real and is related to where the subject is standing in relation to the center of the vortex.

Leaning into the Center of the Vortex

This phenomenon is a strange one and somewhat dependent on an individual's inner ear. All of the attractions demonstrate this leaning inside their crooked shacks. This is not the best place to perform this experiment, because people are compensating for the crooked floor and cannot feel if they are applying even pressure on their feet in order to stand up straight. The slanted walls throw off your equilibrium, so it can be argued that there is little value in comparing standing people. But the Oregon Vortex® and the Mystery Spot both demonstrated they can balance a common broom on the floor, and it will remain "standing" for many hours. This is something that cannot happen in normal space and time. So some force is acting on the broom to stabi-

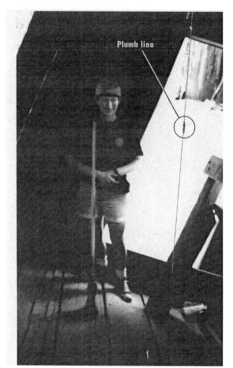

Plumb line

Figure 9: The standing broom is about 7° off from the plum line. The plumb line has been enhanced, so as to be seen.

lize it, permitting it to stay erect for hours. Figure 9 shows such a broom. You can see a plumb line to the right of the standing broom. The observer will see a 7° tilt towards the center.

Evidence for a Vortex

The underlying cause for this distortion is higher concentrations of information being directed to this area in time and space. The full explaination with theoretical background will be given in Chapter 6. This "force" is happening in another dimension and therefore very difficult to measure directly. The time measurements are one measurment tool we have used to quantify this vortex, but archological information will have to be collected to settle the issue. The bending of tree limbs and the twisting of tree trunks are another indication that a vortex of energy or information is present in these gravitational anomalies.

The madrona tree in Figure 10 has grown in a counter-clockwise curlicue. Also shown is a tree whose limb has grown curved along some force line, bends in a clock-wise direction around the center. Other trees were observed bent in a clockwise direction in the vortex. The tree limbs, at some point, started growing in an arch. Then, the arching growth would stop and the tree started growing straight up again.

The reason this phenomenon may be proof of a vortex type action is because tree growth is caused, on a molecular level, by gibberellins which are plant hormones produced by most higher plants. Something is acting as a force or time distortion that is

Figure 10: Bent and twisted trees in the Oregon Vortex.

fooling the growth patterns of some trees. The fur and pine trees may not be as susceptible as the madrona, but I have seen fur trees grow at one angle, then change to straight up. The explaination for this phenomenon is in Chapter 7.

Other Phenomena Reported

Five years ago I got a headache while working in the vortex. I asked the manager if some visitors had reported headaches or other unusual health events. What he reported was that some people do report they have gotten a headache while in the vortex. Others have reported that other pains they had disappeared while inside the vortex. Both of these reported phenomena are explained in Chapter 7.

[1]There are a number a reasons why I believe the shack was originally built as a tourist attraction. There is no evidence that there were ever windows or doors places in the openings of the shack. I notices no nail holes and the window openings were not a standard size. If this shack was truly an assay office and tool shed, it would have certainly

had windows and doors. There is no room partition, to speak of, between the two rooms. There is no physical way the shack could have slid down the hillside and stay intact. I had walked up the hill and saw no evidence of a former foundation or evidence of an earth slide. There are many trees just east and up the hill from the building. Some are large tall evergreens that I estimate are at least 80 years old. The shack could not have slid down the hill and not been stopped by one of those trees. There is a picture in Litster's notes, that looks like it was taken in the 1930s, of the shack looking fairly new. The window and door openings are approximately square and the building shows no visible damage. I can not image a simple wooden shack sliding 40' down a hill and showing no outwardly damage. Finally the age of the shack in Litster's picture (which is the same shack there today) is too young to be one build by a mining company 16 or more years before.

[2]In the first four pages of Litster's Notes and Data booklet (©1953) he introduces a confusing number of traditional scientific terms used in the 1940s and 50s but does not philosophically explain how these terms apply to the phenomena observed in the vortex. For instance he introduces the concept that this area is a vortex but gives no proof for how he came to this conclusion. The definition of a vortex is: a mass of fluid having a circular motion tending to form a vacuum in the center, drawing objects to the center that are caught in the vortex. I don't disagree with this idea but he gives no explanation why he thinks it is a vortex. Then he associates terrestrial magnetism and electromagnetism as being a vortex which is not naturally true. Only high density gravitational fields can be analogous to a vortex. He finally concludes the field of the vortex is electromagnetic in nature and the observer should expect to see changes in "the light field and other fields." Again he does not explain how he came to this conclusion or does he put it in the framework of a theory for the vortex. One of the things he is wrong about is that electromagnetic fields do not alter time or change the size of objects. Only strong gravitational fields do that. He uses the electron microscope as an analogy to what is causing the optical changes in height. The problem with this explanation is the amount of voltage used in an electron-microscope is greater than 20,000 volts. If there were any kind of high voltage streams present in the vortex, all electronic circuits in cameras, radios, frequency counters, computers, would be fried and that just is not happening. Finally he tells us that observations made by scientific instruments are of no value because of some incomprehensible reason he gives.

[3]I can find no reference to the concept of terralines in geophysics. He presents no reference or proof for terralines or what would cause then on the earth. He says he finds these lines when an individual leans more north when they come in contact with one of them. This form of testing is just too subjective to be of any scientific use. The geometric model of terralines laid out in the form of a grid is totally different to the stricture of a vortex. Finally he says the vortex field and the terralines are both energy-wave forms at 90° from each other. But again he does not explain how he determined these forces are an energy-wave nor does he define the energy-wave. This leads me to believe he was just grasping for straws to explain these phenomena.

[4]The Lorenz transformation for the size of an ob,ject calculates a 5.4% shrinkage represents an object traveling at 58,863 miles per second. A 5.8% shrinkage represents an object traveling at 60,832 miles per second.

[5]I had spoken to Terry Cooper and his employees after they received the first proof of this book. He expressed concern and did not like the fact that my findings were contradictory in some cases to Litster's findings. They have presented to the world that they alone had the explanation for these phenomena and the other Mystery Spots were copies at best. He also did not seem to understand the explanation and philosophy presented in this book. To settle the issue I offered to drive down to Gold Hill and retest the vortex for the shrink and grow by photographing the entire vortex and producing a series of photographs that would look like Figure 19b (page 47). This test would have settled the issue once and for all and it was quantifiable. I had not originally tested the north side of the vortex to see the amount of shrink and grow present there. When I arrived there on August 10, he refused to let me preform the test. So I can only assume he has something to hide and I will continue to assume my model of the vortex and the shrink and grow phenomenon are correct.

Chapter 3

Confusion Hill

Confusion Hill is located at 75001 North Hwy. 101, Piercy, California. It was originally a logging camp. The shack was constructed in 1949 as a tourist attraction by its developer George Hudson. The two-room shack seems to be modeled after the Oregon Vortex shack.

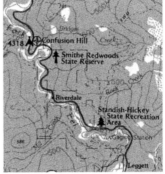

Figure 11: Location map of Confusion Hill, Piercy California.

The operators of the attraction say the gravitational anomaly appears to be about 100′ in diameter. The scope of our experiment was such that it was not intended to measure variation in the vortexes' size.

The Start of the Experiment

We arrived at the attraction at 11:26 AM on June 6, 1996. A new 9 volt battery was put into the crystal frequency source. It was 12:10 PM when the frequency counter, cable, and crystal was set up. The frequency counter was turned on for about twenty minutes before it was connected to the crystal via the cable. Both, I believe were outside the vortex. We spent about 30 minutes probing the vortex looking for the center. At first it was not known whether the frequency would shift up or down near the center. I did notice the fluctuation in the frequency counter when the crystal was first introduced near and in the vortex. I began to call this phenomenon the "Jell-O effect" which I will explain in-depth in Chapter 7.

There was no tour guide in the attraction and the store manager did not know where the center was or where the edges of the anomaly were.

Time Fluctuation Results

The frequency counter was placed at 90' away from what was thought to be the center. Only the 113' coax cable was used. At 12:52 PM the experiment started.

Experimental test run number 1 started at 12:52 PM. Measurement started at the 75' mark and proceeded toward the center in a west to east direction. The frequency counter started at 24,997,977 Hz. The graphs only display the last four numbers (7,977 Hz.). The frequency inside was lower than outside by 27 hertz. The lowest frequency was reached at the 20' mark.

Frequency

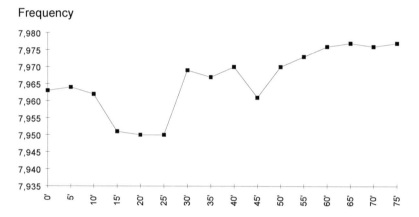

Table 13: Run number 1; measuring frequency from the 75' mark into the center of the vortex using 113' of cable. Start time: 12:52 PM. Duration of the experiment: 7 minutes.

The second run (Table 14) started at the 75' mark and then proceeded to the center. The frequency inside was lower than outside, but the frequency range was only 9 hertz over 75', so no conclusion can be reached in this run.

The third run (Table 15) started at the 75' mark and proceeded to the center and then 10 feet beyond. The frequency inside was lower than outside by 27 hertz. The lowest frequency was reached at the 10' mark. At the 35' mark there was a frequency fluctuation ranging from 24,997,998 to 24,998,128 hertz. Another fluctuation occurred at 10' and 5' but was only 6 hertz and 2 hertz, respectively. The frequency difference between outside and inside was 69 hertz. This was a fairly large difference.

The fourth run (Table 16) measured from the center, then out to the 70′ mark. The frequency went down, as the crystal

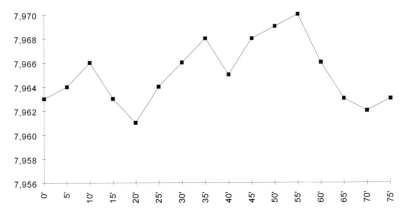

Table 14: Run number 2; measuring frequency from the 75′ mark into the center of the vortex using 113′ of cable. Start time: 1:06 PM. Duration of the experiment: 8 minutes.

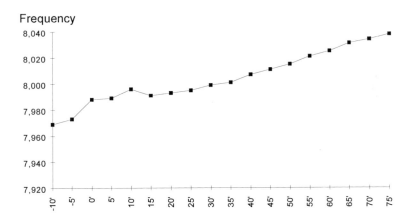

Table 15: Run number 3; measuring frequency from the 75′ mark to -10′ mark of the vortex using 113′ of cable. Start time: 1:33 PM. Duration of the experiment: 16 minutes.

was brought outside of the anomaly. This was the first time, at this location, that the frequency changed direction uniformly. The frequency difference between inside and out was 9 hertz.

This is not much of a difference, but the frequency counter was very stable and it was recording a real change.

We performed another run outside of the vortex and per-

Frequency

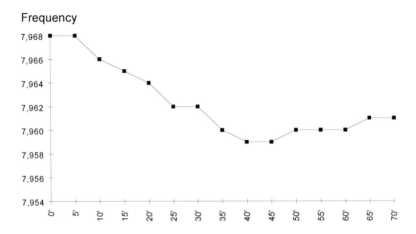

Table 16: Run number 4; measuring frequency from the center to the 70' mark of the vortex. Start time 1:50 PM. Duration of the experiment 7 minutes.

pendicular to the center to see if the equipment was performing properly and get another check, as to where the edge of the vortex was. That experiment started at 2:05 PM and lasted 10 minutes. Measurements were taken every 10', starting at 80' south of the gift shop and going to the back of the gift shop. There is a twisted redwood tree at the back of the gift shop (Figure 15) so some influence is present there. The result of that run was the frequency went from 24,997,961 at the 80' mark to 24,997,964 by the twisted tree. A difference of only 4 hertz. So I was pretty confident we were getting good data.

Dynamic Change

After my observations at the Oregon Vortex I added one experiment, that being measuring for dynamic changing over time. The crystal was left at the 20' mark for 2 hours and 40 minutes. Table 17 shows the frequency changes over that time period. The frequency change was 37 hertz.

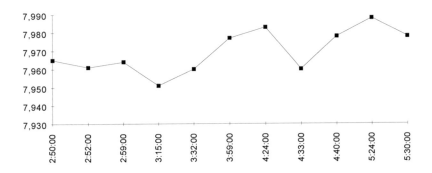

Table 17: Measuring frequency from the 20' mark from the center of the vortex using 113' of cable. The experiment started at: 3:16 PM. Duration of the experiment: 160 minutes.

Force Moving a Dead Weight

The operators of this attraction report that it was harder pushing a dead weight towards the center than away from it. I used the ceiling on the shack to hang our 25 lb. weight. My assistant, Vic Ardelean, held the ruler flat and read off the distances (Figure 12). We could not set up my weight suspension device, because there was no level ground large enough to set it up and not get in the way of tourists. This setup worked just fine. Tables 18 and 19 shows the force, in pounds, to move the 25lb. weight 5", 10", and 15" towards and away from the center of the anomaly. The center of the vortex was to the south of us. Table 18 was taken at a location 20' farther north and farther away from the center and it took 11% more force to move the weight towards the center. Table 19 was closer to where I be-

Lbs.   Lbs.

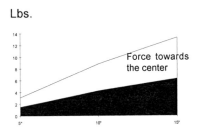

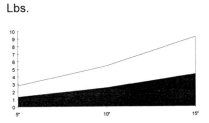

Table 18: Graph showing the force in pounds to move a 25 lb. weight 5", 10", and 15". First location in the cabin.

Table 19: Graph showing the force in pounds to move a 25 lb. weight 5", 10", and 15". Second location in the cabin.

Figure 12: Vic Ardelean holding the ruler for the weight expiment.

lieve the center was. It shows 13% more force necessary to move the 25 lb. weight. The black area is the force away from the center. The explanation for this phenomenon is in Chapter 7.

Shrink and Grow Phenomenon

As mentioned in Chapter 2, the main attraction of these tourist sites is the shrink and grow phenomenon. When two people stand on opposite sides of a level plank, then change positions, the observers, perpendicular to the subjects, see the change in heights. The problem with this attraction is there is not enough level ground to set up our plank close to the center of the vortex. The area of greatest height change was on the west end of the shack. Figures 13 and 14 shows a 3.57% shrink and grow effect over only 2.5′. The size difference would probably be greater, if we could have stood farther apart. I set up the tripod and camera in the cabin, because there was not enough room to get both of us in the photograph. The tripod was perpendicular to the center of the concrete slab and I did check that the slab was level. I estimate the center of the vortex was about 25′ from us.

The second location tested was about 45′ from the center of the vortex and 30′ from the back of the gift shop. We recorded no shrink and grow phenomenon. The attraction has pictures at this location showing a 10% shrink effect, but the problem with the photos are the camera is not perpendicular to the center of the slab, and the camera moved between shots. Most are taken from the end farther away from the center, which will accentuate the effect. There is a possibility that we tried photographing

Figure 13: Author is standing to the right and farther away from the center of the anomaly. Vic Ardelean is the other person.

Figure 14: Author is standing to the left and closer to the center of the anomaly. He gets 3.57% smaller over a dis-tance of 2.5′. Using Lorenz's transformation, an object traveling at 48,488.7miles per second will get 3.57% smaller.

this phenomenon just when the field was changing, and so no effect would be noticeable. The Oregon Vortex had reported this happening, so it is a common occurrence. We just don't know when it happens.

Leaning into the Center of the Vortex

This phenomenon was tested, but we could not see any meaningful difference between the plumb line and person trying to stand erect. The slanted walls and floor do not help matters. There was no broom there, or with us, to test a standing broom compared to the plumb line, like at the Oregon Vortex and the Mystery Spot.

Evidence for a Vortex

The bending of tree limbs and the twisting of tree trunks may be an indication a vortex of energy is present in the anomaly.

Figure 15 shows a large, twisted redwood tree located in the back of the gift shop. The trunk of the tree grew in a counter-clockwise curlicue   Other trees were observed growing at one angle, then changing and resuming a vertical growth pattern.

Figure 15: Bent and twisted trees at Confusion Hill in back of the gift shop.

The types of trees in this area are much different than at the Oregon Vortex, but the "force" effected the redwoods. In Figure 16 is the base of a large redwood located on the southeast side of the shack. The turnbuckles shown on the tree are helping to hold up the crooked shack. As you can see, the tree trunk is twisted counter-

Figure 16: Twisted redwood tree trunk in back of the shack.

clockwise. This phenomenon is having an effect on the growth patterns of the tree at a molecular level. Trees were observed tilted clockwise around the center of the anomaly. A complete explanation is in Chapter 7.

Other Phenomena Reported

The manager told us that some visitors have reported headaches inside the anomaly. This reported phenomenon is explained in Chapter 7.

Chapter 4
The Mystery Spot

The Mystery Spot is located at 465 Mystory Spot Rd. (off Bran-ciforte Dr.), Santa Cruz, California. It was originally discovered in 1940 by an individual who purchased the land to build a mountain home on. While surveying the hillside, they noticed their compass was way off. They claim that a compass can be 10° to 90° off. The operators say that the owners had drilled a 1500-foot hole in front of the anomaly, but found no iron or other metal that would affect their instruments. The original owners constructed a two room shack in the 1940s for the tourists. The two room shack is constructed just like the Oregon Vortex shack. I can't help but think that the Mystery Spot shack was modeled after the Oregon Vortex, including building it crooked on the side of the hill.

Figure 17: Location maps of The Mystery Spot, Santa Cruz, California.

The operators say the gravitational anomaly is about 150' in diameter. I believe the diameter may be about 200', because where we found the center. The scope of the experiment did not try to measure variation in the vortexes' size.

The Start of the Experiment

We arrived at the attraction at 12:45 PM on June 7, 1996. A new 9-volt battery was put into the crystal frequency source. It was 1:53 PM when the frequency counter, the 113' cable, and crystal were set up. The frequency counter was turned on one hour before it was connected to the crystal via the cable. The frequency counter was placed behind the gift shop on a concrete path and 20' outside the vortex. We spent about 53 minutes probing the vortex looking for the center. I again noticed the same fluctuation in the frequency counter when the crystal was first introduced into the vortex. For the first 3 minutes the counter read a frequency swing of over 500 hertz. After a short while, it went from 24,998,042 to 24,998,146 over 3 minutes. After about 15 minutes of that, we started probing the anomaly to locate the center. Over a distance of 113′ from the counter, the frequency went from 24,998,042 to 24,998,092, closer to the center (50 hertz difference). At this time I began to think that the "Jell-O effect" was real. I began to develop a theory of why this was happening. The final clue at the Oregon Vortex on June 9 confirmed my hunch. The explanation is in Chapter 7.

Time Fluctuation Results

After I determined the center was on the other side of the crooked shack, we moved the equipment up the hill through some thick underbrush. We then went far enough up the hill to be about 100′ away. A new 9-volt battery was put into the crystal source box, because at that time I wasn't sure whether or not the frequency fluctuation was due to battery problems or what. The frequency counter was placed at 110′ away from what was thought to be the center. Only the 113′ coax cable was used. At 3:31 PM the experiment started.

The first test run (Table 20) measurement indicated the frequency inside the anomaly was higher than the outside. The total adjusted frequency difference was 16 hertz. We located

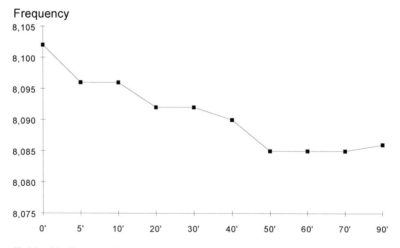

Table 20: Run number 1; measuring frequency from the 90′ mark into the center of the vortex using 113′ of cable. Start time: 3:31 PM. Duration of the experiment: 7 minutes.

the approximate center near the base of a twisted eucalyptus tree (Figure 23). The center was about 10′ west of the south end of the shack.

The second run started at 3:47 PM in the center of the vortex and then proceeded back out to the 90′ mark. Frequency did not shift very much at all (5 hertz over 7 minutes), The frequency inside was lower (24,998,105 Hz.) than outside (24,998,110 Hz) but the frequency changed at the 30′ mark, so no conclusion could be reached in this run. It may be the overall frequency of the vortex had changed from one run to the next.

For the third run (Table 21), we decided to move the equipment to the front of the attraction. This was about 20′ from the edge of the vortex where we were before. This was done because the working conditions on the backside were too difficult to deal with. We were set up again by 4:44 PM near the gift shop. I connected the two cables together, so we had 313′ of coax to

Frequency

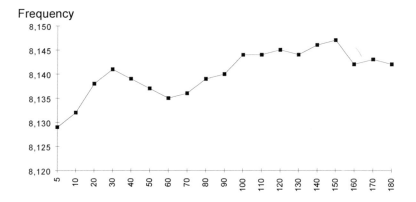

Table 21: Run number 3; measuring frequency from the counter to the shack. Start time: 4:44 PM. Duration of the experiment: 26 minutes.

stretch out. In run number 3, the frequency went down towards the center, as it did during run 2. The direct distance to the center from the frequency counter was more like 150′, but we could not go straight, because there were fences and buildings in our way. The distance listed here is more like the amount of cable stretched out. We did have the 100′ tape measure stretched out but that went just so far. We had to mark off every ten feet with stakes to get our distances. The 170′ mark was by the back fence near the center of the vortex and the 180′ mark was inside the shack. The total frequency difference was 18 hertz.

Dynamic Change

The last frequency/time experiment was to leave the crystal at 40′ away from the center and record the frequency changes over a long period of time. The times were recorded randomly because we were doing other experiments at the same time. Table 22 shows the frequency changes over seven hours and thirteen minutes. At the 3:29 hour mark, I moved the frequency counter 50′ further outside. The employees let me plug the frequency counter into their power line. That may be why the frequency dropped down. It's not due to the frequency counter not being at its ambient temperature but rather it may have been influenced by some time distortion caused by a coronal effect that Litster writes about. The frequency difference between high and low was 56 hertz. This experiment is definitely showing there are frequency changes occurring over long periods of time.

The next morning at 8:03 AM, I put a new 9-volt battery into the crystal frequency source and started reading the results for the next 69 minutes. Table 23 shows the frequency first rising over 35 minutes, then decreasing for the rest of the time. This pattern shows that the frequencies are dynamically changing during the day. Sometimes going down, other times reversing.

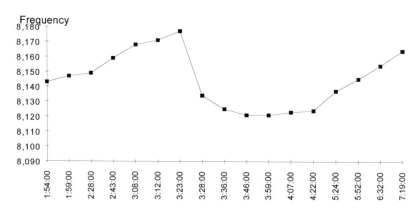

Table 22: Measuring frequency from the 40′ mark from the center of the vortex using 313′ of cable. The experiment started at: 5:14 PM. Duration of the experiment: 5 hours and 25 minutes.

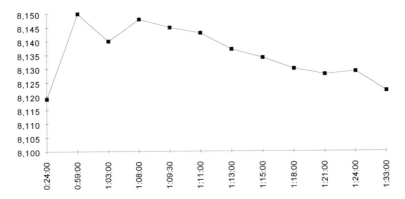

Table 23: Measuring frequency from the 40′ mark from the center of the vortex, using 313′ of cable. The experiment started at: 8:03 AM. Duration of the experiment: 69 minutes.

Force Moving a Dead Weight

The operators of the attraction report that it was harder pushing a dead weight towards the center than away from it. I used their 18 lb. weight, which was hanging from the ceiling. My assistant held the ruler flat and read off the distances. Tables 24 and 25 show the force, in pounds, to move the 18 lb. weight 5", 10", and 15" towards and away from the center of the anomaly. Table 24 shows a southwest and northeast direction which is more closely aligned to the center of the vortex. The center of the vortex was southwest of our location. It took 58% more force to move the weight 15" towards the center than away. Table 25 is an east-west direction showing 15% greater force moving the weight towards the west. The explanation for this phenomenon is in Chapter 7.

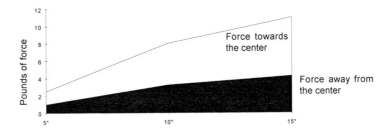

Table 24: Graph showing the force in pounds to move an 18 lb. weight 5", 10", and 15" in a southwest direction.

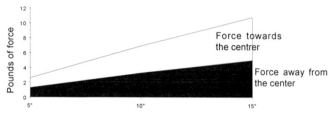

Table 25: Graph showing the force in pounds to move a 18 lb. weight 5", 10", and 15". East-west direction.

Shrink and Grow Phenomenon

The main attraction of the site is the shrink and grow phenomenon. The area of greatest height change was by the courtyard to the south of the shack. Figures 18 and 19a show a 4.2% shrink and grow effect over only 7'. Figure 19b shows just the poles, brought together, that were 7.5' apart. They clearly show a 5.24% height difference. The tripod was perpendicular to the center of the board and I did check that the platform was level. I estimate the center of the vortex was about 15' from us.

The second location tested was about 35' from the center of the vortex and was in a north-south direction. There is a concrete slab shaped like a T. We found no shrink and grow phe-

Figure 18: Author is standing to the right and farther away from the center of the anomaly. Vic Ardelene is the other person.

Figure 19a: Author is standing to the left and closer to the center of the anomaly. He gets 4.2% smaller over a distance of 7'.

Figure 19b: Shows just the measuring poles that were 7.5' apart. The base was even. The 5.24% hight difference is clearly shown.

Figure 20: Picture of a standing broom with a plumb line showing the difference. Courtesy of The Mystery Spot.

nomenon there. The reason was that being the slab is laid out perpendicular to the center, so there is no time or information differential. The slab should be pointing towards the center, as the previous one did.

Leaning into the Center of the Vortex

This phenomenon was tested and a small observable difference of about 4° was noticed. I have included a photo, courtesy of the Mystery Spot that shows a better example of this phenomenon. The difference shown in Figure 20 is about 7°, which is about the same reported at the Oregon Vortex.

Figure 21: Bent young redwood. In the vortex.

Figure 22: Below and right: Slanted trees to the north of the center of the vortex.

Evidence for a Vortex

The bending of tree limbs and the twisting of tree trunks are present at all three gravitational anomalies. The tree limbs bend clock-wise around the center of the vortex and some trees display a counter-clockwise curlicue in their trunk. The four types of trees at this location are the redwood, pine, madrona, and eucalyptus trees. Figure 21 shows some small redwood trees curving while growing in a clock-wise direction around the vortex. Some of the larger redwood trees demonstrate two different growth patterns. First, they grow leaning in a clock-wise direction; then two-thirds up they change, and grow straight up. Figure 22 shows some eucalyptus and redwoods growing curved in the same clock-wise direction. Figure 23 shows a large, twisted eucalyptus tree located in the back of the shack and near the center. It has grown like a curlicue.

Figure 23: Eucalyptus tree growing with a counter-clock-wise curlicue in trunk. Located very near the center of the vortex.

Two Curlicue Trees

Other Phenomena Reported

The long-time guide told us that some visitors have reported headaches inside the anomaly. Others had commented that pain they had before they entered the vortex had disappeared. These reported phenomena are explained in Chapter 7.

Chapter 5
Magnetic Hill

Magnetic Hill is a stretch of road on Lichau Road, east of Rohnert Park, California (see Figure 24 and 25). It's a 300' stretch of country road starting 100' east of the cattle crossing (Figure 26). It's on the side of a hill, and no large trees to see if there are any bent and curlicue tree trunks. In

Figure 26, I superimposed onto the photograph some markers to help identify location of the phenomena. The phenomena starts about where the first white line is, and ends where the second white line is in the background. The white circle in the middle of the road is approximately where the center is.

Figure 24: Location maps of Magnetic Hill, east of Rohnert Park, California.

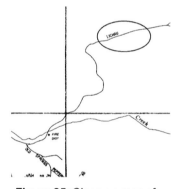

Figure 25: Close-up map of Magnetic Hill.

Figure 26: Looking east on Lichau Road. The cattle crossing is in the foreground.

What is Happening Here?

What the local people have noticed is that if you stop your car along this stretch of road and put it in neutral, your car will roll westward, up the slight incline towards the cattle crossing. Figures 27 through 30 show the incline to the road. Figure 27 was taken, looking eastward, with the camera on our measuring stick laying flat on the cattle crossing. I checked the cattle crossing and found it to be absolutely level. Figure 28 was taken by the second white line (about 400' east of the cattle crossing), and it is looking west towards the cattle crossing. Figure 29 was taken near the center, looking west towards the cattle crossing. Figure 30 was taken from the middle, looking east. As you can see from all three pictures, it appears the road is slop-

Figure 27: Lichau Road looking east.

Figure 28: Lichau Road looking west from the eastern edge of the anomaly. The road looks like it is sloping up but it is not.

Figure 29: Lichau Road looking west from the approximate middle.

ing upwards towards the cattle crossing. It's not; rather, it is sloping downward towards the cattle crossing.

The series of photos in Figure 31 show us test sampling the length of the road for 400' from the cattle crossing going east.

Figure 30: Lichau Road looking east from the approximate middle.

Pictures were taken about every 35' apart. As is shown, the entire length of that road is sloping down towards the cattle crossing, not up. The slope is opposite to what the eye sees.

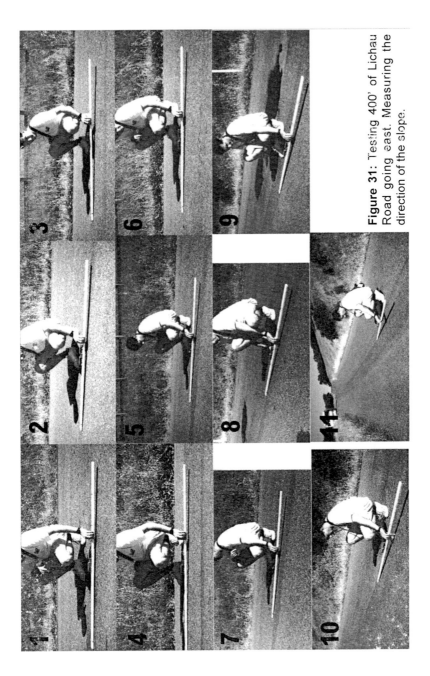

Figure 31: Testing 400' of Lichau Road going east. Measuring the direction of the slope.

The Frequency Experiments

We arrived at the location about 3:45 PM on June 5, 1996. A new 9 volt battery was put into the crystal frequency source. It was 4:53 PM when the frequency counter, the 313' cable, and crystal were set up. The frequency counter was turned on for 30 minutes before it was connected to the crystal. The frequency counter was first placed 40' in from the camper. After a frequency shift was located, the counter was moved to where the second white line is, located in Figure 26. We spent about 41 minutes probing the anomaly looking for the center. The frequency outside the area read 24,997,829 Hz. As the crystal entered the gravitational anomaly, the frequency rose to 24,997,904 Hz ±5 hertz. Towards the middle, the frequency dropped to 24,997,890 Hz. There isn't much difference within the area, but there was a difference. If there is a vortex like the other one tested, the road may be going through a part of a much larger circle. The center of the possible vortex could be up the hill or down.

Other Locations

I have found two other locations reporting the same phenomenon as Magnetic Hill. One is Spook Hill in Lake Wales, Florida. The road looks like its going up hill, but the cars are rolling up the hill. The street looks like it has a dip in the middle of it, but really there isn't one at all. It is sloping downward.

The second location is Magnetic Hill in Moncton, New Brunswick, Canada. The same phenomenon is present. Figure

Figure 32: Magnetic Hill in Moncton, New Brunswick, Canada.

32 shows a dip in the road and a car rolling backwards, seemingly up the hill.

All three locations are probably caused by the same thing. The question is: What could cause such as large distortion in our time and space, and still be localized to a relatively small area? Chapter 6 presents an information theory of existence that may have the answer for all of this.

We of course wanted to see if Vic's 6,000 lb. motor home would coast up hill. We put it in neutral and stopped by the eastern end at what looked level. The camper started rolling until it reached 10 mph. It did start slowing down before the cattle crossing.

Shrink and Grow Phenomenon

We tested for this phenomenon but found no visible effect. We tried standing east-west, as well as north-south, but no size change was visible.

Evidence for a Vortex

There were no trees in the area, so no observation of bending tree limbs was possible. Since there are no trees there, I would say that there is insufficient information to draw any conclusions of the area. All we do know is that there is a gravitational distortion and a crystal frequency generator is slightly affected.

Chapter 6
The Theory of Multidimensional Reality

I claimed in the Introduction that the reason why traditional science ignores phenomena like these gravitational anomalies is because their philosophy of science cannot explain their existence. Their science is wrong, because the foundation of their philosophy is—that matter is the dominant thing in the universe.

Their philosophy isn't a new idea. It was first expressed by Greek atomists, like Leucippus (440 B.C.) and Democritus (420 B.C.). They taught that nothing exists, except atoms and the great void. Plato's book *The Sophist* says

"Some of them (the atomists) drag down everything from heaven and the invisible to earth, actually grasping rocks and trees with their hands; for they lay their hands on all such things and maintain stoutly that that alone exists which can be touched and handled; for they define existence and body, or matter, as identical, and if anyone says that anything else, which has no body, exists, they despise him utterly, and will not listen to any other theory than their own."[1]

The philosophies and attitudes of the atomists most closely resemble the philosophies and behavior of modern-day scientists and academia. Solon, Plato, and the Jews fought this kind of philosophy for hundreds of years. Today nobody in academia even questions it. The atomists have won.

The purpose of this chapter is to explain what is an *Information Theory of Existence* and give you enough supporting analogies, proofs, and descriptions that you have a working knowledge of the concept. Then, you can understand what is causing the phenomena observed at these gravitational anomalies, which will be explained in Chapter 7. These locations may result in the greatest discovery in history!

I have divided this chapter into three sections. The first defines the problem. The second explains the *Theory of Multidimensional Reality* with analogies to help you understand it. The third is scientific explanations of some phenomena, as support-

ing proofs of the theory. If you want a more detailed explanation of, ancient philosophical sources, and causes of the ice ages,
you can order: *God's Day of Judgment, the Real Cause of Global
Warming,* from Vector Associates, POB 40135, Bellevue, WA
98015 ($24.95 paperback; $34.95 hardbound).

The Problem

What is a Philosophy?

A philosophy is a collection of ideas that is supposed to
create a model that helps you understand the universe around
you. If your model of the universe is wrong, you will have a
much harder time understanding the phenomena you see. What
is wrong with the modern-day philosophy of science is that matter
is not the dominant thing in the universe, but rather information
is. There are only two ways you can try to explain the universe.
One is that matter is the dominant thing in the universe; the
other is that, information is the dominant thing in the universe.
As far as I know, these are the only two approaches one can
take. Unfortunately, academia has chosen the wrong path.

Since 1977, when I wrote *Reality Revealed, The Theory of Multidimensional Reality,* people have asked me: Why did I figure out
this great mystery and all the others haven't? The answer I give
them is this analogy. Imagine you have a 10,000-piece puzzle
with random shapes and colors; but, collectively, they form a
larger coherent picture. To make matters worse, you don't have
a picture of what this thing is supposed to look like, when all the
pieces are put together. The picture is like a philosophy. If you
don't have a philosophy, or you have the wrong picture then you
don't know where the pieces are supposed to go. Without the
correct picture you need tens of thousands of people working
thousands of hours to try to piece the puzzle together. I just
have a better picture than they do.

Man has dealt with the questions of existence and being
throughout his history. What is existence? What is being? What
is reality? These three questions have been asked by wise men
through the ages. Many philosophical discussions have taken
place on the subject. Unfortunately, the men that pondered these
questions were limited by their knowledge. The experiences one

has throughout a lifetime are the limiting factors that allow a person to abstract, conceptualize, or analogize in this reality. These experiences are the tools that allowed man to crawl through his dark cave and make sense out of the flashes of light, the dim shadows, the faint sounds, which struck him constantly but were rarely perceived.

Commentary on the Field of Science Today

Science, using their model of the universe, has made little headway in understanding the most basic phenomena in our reality; phenomena like electromagnetism, magnetism, gravity, and light. Unless you understand what these are, you will not be able to understand what existence is. Presently the traditional theories are only workable over a narrow framework. Many scientists have found that their discipline breaks down at the limits. Then another scientist comes along to try to increase the area that that discipline can explain. However, no one has been able to explain the total picture or even to define the most basic definitions of their discipline.

Why has an Information Theory of Existence Eluded Us?

An Information Theory of Existence hadn't been discovered before 1977, because it was so hard to conceptualize for humans. Without the videotape and computer analogies, it's almost impossible to understand.

I will give you an electronic analogy that will define the problem. Imagine you are looking at a television. Now let's say, for this discussion, that this is a holographic TV that can project a three-dimensional image. Now lets say you are looking at a man, a woman, and a outdoor country scene on this television. You know that the images you are looking at do not originate only within that TV. The information for the image is stored on a one dimensional-like media called videotape. The video player converts the magnetic information into electromagnetic information. Then, it is transmitted out from the TV station's antenna to your TV receiver. Your TV reconstructs the images that you now see. The end result is this picture of a man, a woman, and a pastoral scene.

Now imagine that you are one of those people in the television. How do you know that you are a created image and that your existence comes from somewhere else? This is the problem, and now you know why it had not been figured out until my book in 1977.

The Theory of Multidimensional Reality

The essence of the problem we face is going from the finite to the infinite. In order for our finite minds to approach the infinite, we have to use all of our resources. We have been taught that infinity cannot be understood by the finite mind. We have been taught that some concepts are beyond the minds of men. I am going to show that this is not true, that the complexity of the universe comes only from an inaccurate picture of reality. To understand infinity is to understand only what the basic systems are. You can't understand the basic systems, unless you have a definite understanding of the underlying philosophies that make up the system.

The Reflexiveness of the Universe

The assumption I make is that everything is related. The truth is all around us. The truth can be found in nature; it can be found in the total man and in his technologies. The complete underlying principles of existence can be found in everything. However, I will show that the only way to understand these principles is to destroy the categorical mind and to develop, instead, a creative mind.

Our universe has underlying principles from which it operates. Everything in the universe has to adhere to the same principles. Everything in the universe is a reflection of everything else. Only the way these reflections hit our senses determines the individuality of entities. Since man is a function of the universe, his structure must also conform to the underlying principles of the universe. Our physical and mental structures are microsystems of the universe. This is much like modern day integrated circuits, which operate on the same principles as the older tube circuits. The integrated circuit is a refinement of the old tube circuit, just as man is a refinement of his universe. Man is smaller than his universe, but the underlying principles are still the same. Even the microscopic structures that make up man, or the integrated circuit structures, are a reflection of what they make up; they, in turn, reflect everything else in the universe. This, in effect, links us with every other thing in the universe. Since our minds and our senses are functions of the universe, they reflect the universe. The universe is also a reflection of our mind and senses.

If this sounds too far out, just think of how we came into being. We began as one cell and a sperm. The resulting zygote contained 46 chromosomes. The DNA molecule had all the information on how every cell was to be formed and where it was to be in relation to everything else, and how the cell was to function and when. Is the information that makes us up stored only in 46 chromosomes? Is this where the information that makes us up ends? Where is the information stored about how the amino acids, that make up the DNA, are to be made? What about the atoms that make's up the amino acids? Behind the underlying principles that determine everything is a creative force. The effect of this creative force can be seen everywhere.

The Basic Theory

The Theory of Multidimensional Reality is a simple idea to explain. It just takes time to understand it. About twenty years ago, a close friend (Gary Sultan) and myself were talking about, what if someone could come up with the secret of the universe, how long would the paper be to explain it. I thought it would be at least a 50 page thesis. My friend thought it could fit on one index card. He was right. It can fit on that index card with room to spare. How the universe works distills down to these two sentences:

1. Everything in the universe is made up of information that exists in another time-space relationship that acts like a computer.
2. The operating system and the one who created the information is God, and as long as He thinks the universe, it exists.

From these two simple sentences you can "build" the model that explains the universe.

The Theory of Multidimensional Reality is a simple idea. The reason why it is called Multidimensional Reality is because it says that an object exists in three different dimensions almost at the same time. I will explain the "almost" later. Multidimensional Reality holds that everything in the universe is made up of information that is stored in the first dimension. The information is stored in a computer-like structure, which I call the "Diehold." (The name *Diehold* was a created name because there was no word that expressed this kind of concept.) The information from the Diehold is then transmitted into the second dimension, which is the transmission dimension. Finally, the third dimension is when the information becomes a piece of matter like an atom.

Life forms are fourth dimensional existences. The consciousness for a person exists in the first dimension, as a separate domain of information; you can call this your soul. What life is, is when the information that makes up your soul is transmitted to the same coordinates as the information that makes up your physical body. In turn, death would be the separation of the two signals. That is why the tunnel of light is seen by those who have clinically died and come back.

The theory defines dimensions differently. The traditional definition of dimensions is length, width, depth, and time. Multidimensional Reality has eight dimensions. The first three are the same as the traditional explanation, but the fourth dimension to the eight are defined by how much potential, and therefore, information an object can collect, control, or perceive. The term potential is synonymous with voltage or electromagnetic potential. The definition for the first four are explained below:

- *The First Dimension* is the storage dimension. There time has no meaning. The Diehold is timeless, even though the Diehold itself is made up of matter but is in another time-space relationship, so it is not perceivable by the creation it forms. It is the information in it that is timeless.
- *The Second Dimension* is the transmission dimension. Time still has no relevance because the transmission is instantaneous.
- *The Third Dimension* is the world of inanimate matter. From atoms to mountains.
- *The Fourth Dimension*—The world of living things. A soul "married" to a physical body. Everything from one-celled animals to humans. The primary quality is that these life forms must physically touch matter to manipulate it. They must physically act to learn about the world around them.

The following two analogies will give you a working knowledge of the Theory of Multidimensional Reality. I use two because each one has its own forté in explaining some of the phenomena in the universe.

The Video Tape Analogy

If you accept the idea that man is a reflection of the universe, then his inventions are also reflections of his universe.
Let us then take the example of a video tape recorder.

A television camera converts the light images from objects
to electrical impulses. The electrical impulses can then be stored
on magnetic tape. You will notice that the form and dimension
in which the picture is stored is different from the electrical impulses that came from the camera, even though the electrical
impulses also represent the same picture of the object. Let's
take the example a little farther. You have a magnetic tape that
contains the information for a color picture with sound. It is
stored in a form where time stands still. When the tape is played
for broadcast, the information on the tape is again converted to
electrical impulses. The impulses are put into a transmitter where
they again change form to become electromagnetic waves transmitted from the antenna. The picture information is now traveling in a two-dimensional form. There is not only the information for the picture but also other frequencies as well. There is a
center beat frequency, a carrier wave frequency (on which the
picture frequencies are superimposed), a separate frequency for
the sound, and finally a frequency that determines the sweep of
your picture tube. The final image you see is a completely syn-
chronized, two-dimensional reality. All the analogies for our own
existence are combined in this one invention. It seems ironic
that an invention that holds the most analogies to our own existence should be the tool used to mesmerize us with fairy tales.

"Here" in one form may not mean "there" in the same form.
If one examines a piece of videotape closely, with a magnifying
glass, or a conventional microscope, you would see only brown-
ish red iron oxide. No matter how highly you magnify the tape,
you could never see the objects represented by the domains on
the magnetic material. If you could identify the objects represented by the domains, the distances between the domains, which
make up the object, would be microcosmic compared to the

distal relationships in this reality. The frequencies of the colors that represent the object would be at a much lower frequency on the tape and in a totally different relationship to each other compared to their representation in this time reality. There would be no time perspective for the objects represented as domains on the tape. They would be frozen in time in their space. Frozen until passed over by a magnetic tape transducer (head device). This transducer converts magnetic fields of a monolithic structure, iron oxide, into electrical fields. These electrical fields are returned to two-dimensional information, representing a totally different time-space reality from what was physically represented by the domains. If the tape speed were increased, time would seem to be shorter between two events. If the tape speed were reduced, time would seem longer between two events. Neglecting synchronization considerations, if the tape increases, the information reproduced at the receiver would appear physically shorter. That's because the receiver's picture-scan is in real time. The transmitted information is in a shorter time; therefore, there is a shorter object. This is reminiscent of Einsteinian Relativity. The opposite is also true: slowing down the tape makes the object longer. Of course, corrections would have to be made in the synchronization or the image would appear totally unrecognizable.

If an object is taped with an increased tape speed, the object would be represented by more domains on the tape. This represents more information, therefore, more mass. This is the same as increasing the velocity of the object. And so it seems that our representative object not only gets shorter when its velocity increases, but its mass also increases. The Lorenz Transforms seem to describe the same point.

In this analogy of existence, matter is converted to energy and energy to matter. This is all relative to whether the tape is going through the head device to receive an image or transmit an image. The information-domains passed over by the tape transducer (head device) determine the current reality, or existence; and velocity determines time-space relationships. Objects representing large domain areas on the tape could distort the time-space relationships of other objects represented by domains near the large object. This can be represented by beams of light from a star passing by a large mass such as our sun and being displaced in time and space.

Einstein called his theory "The Special Theory of Relativity," because he recognized the speed of light (2.997925 × 10⁸ meters per second) is the constant of the universe and that nothing could go faster than light. There was other relativity theories at the time, so the word "special" identified Einstein's. He theorized that no matter how fast an object was going, if a beam of light was sent out from that object, the velocity of that light would be the same as for an object at rest. This idea was a departure from classical mechanics, which believed in the cumulative effect of velocities. Einstein had no explanation as to what light was at the time he formulated his theory.

The Theory of Multidimensional Reality's explanation for this is: The speed of light is a constant because it is the speed or rate by which the information that makes up the universe, is passing by the "head device." Now I don't want you to think that I'm saying we are all on video tape and everything has been set in time. That is not the case. The Diehold is really acting like a computer so instead of a "head device" there is something that is acting like a CPU but remember I am using an analogy to help explain how the universe works. The tape analogy is the best way of explaining what light and time is, which I will explain later in the proof section.

One might ask, "What does this analogy have to do with our existence? An object on a tape doesn't have self-determination, can't think; the object can't live. It is only an electromagnetic representation of an object, whether the tape is moving or is stopped." Well, for one thing, the videotape analogy shows the universal reflexiveness of existence. The model, at best, is an understandable reflection of the real system.

The Computer Analogy

The computer analogy is very important for revealing the greatest secret there is to be discovered in geophysics, astronomy, and climatology. That secret is the causes of the ice ages, polar reversals, mass extinction's and creation of new species, and why they all happen at the same time geologically.

The Diehold is really a computer, but this computer creates the matter world we live in. Like all computers, the Diehold would have to have clocking, synchronizing, and resynchronizing frequencies. Clocking frequencies are stable oscillator pulses in a synchronous computer, for timing all operations such as gating, recording and printing. The bits of information in a synchronous or sequential computer will wait until a clocking pulse arrives, then the bits of information will proceed to another section of the core memory or to the software. Computers have these frequencies in order to keep the massive amounts of bits of information within specific time slots. All of these various resynchronizing frequencies are timed to the main clock cycle. That's how all digital computers work. Computers have to have these synchronizing frequencies in order to prevent race conditions. That is, when the computer gains or looses bits within a clock cycle. In other words, a computer could not work unless it had these synchronizing frequencies.

Keeping this in mind, remember my example of a holographic TV with two people displayed on it. I pose to you the question: If you are one of those people, how do you know you are really a created existence from another dimension? The answer is, you figure it out by looking for the clocking, synchronizing, and resynchronizing frequencies in your existence. The most important to discover is the main clocking frequency. Once you discover that one, you see its effect throughout the universe.

The building blocks of our matter world are the atoms that make it up. By the Theory the information that makes up matter is transmitted into our existence at digital frequencies above the microwave range and below the infrared spectrum. We will cover that in greater detail later under The Atom, but I want to introduce the concept that a carrier wave is also present and modulated with the frequencies or information that makes up the atom.

The universe has objects that have existed for billions of years, like stars and planets. It has life forms like us, that last about 75-90 years, as well as atoms that may modulate in and out of existence every few milliseconds. The Diehold would have to have controlling frequencies that would be able to control all of them from the longest to the shortest. To give you an example of some of these, there are the sunspot cycles of 11.092 years, and the 88.73 year Gleissberg solar cycle (eight solar cycles). Helioseismology has shown there are many short-term oscillations on the sun. Some as short as 2 minutes, 40 seconds. The earth has a variety of frequencies from a few minutes to weeks. You are probably most familiar with human biorhythms, as well as a myriad of other frequencies associated with our neural-electrical physiology. These cycles show up in everything all the way down to the atom, which I will cover later.

There have been a few books published after *Reality Revealed* that have suggested that some of the subsystems in our universe act like they are a hologram. For instance, the way brains process information is like the holographic storage of information. I am saying the universe **IS** a hologram and that this computer hologram creates the matter world we live in. Since the brain is a reflection of the universe, it therefore operates on the same fundamental principles as the universe.

Some Proofs

The following are explanations of some of the basic phenomena of our universe, using the *Theory of Multidimensional Reality* as an explanation. The scope of this booklet is not to give long, detailed explanations as was done in *Reality Revealed,* or *Secrets of the Universe,* but rather a working understanding of the applications to understand what is happening inside these gravitational anomalies.

Gravity

Gravity was briefly covered in the video tape analogy. The force of gravity is caused by the massive amounts of information that makes up planets or stars, being directed to a point in time and space. Any object that comes within the proximity of this information field will be effected by a "pushing" force towards the center of the modulation point,[2] as well as a time distortion. What is meant by a modulation point is the *xyz* coordinates in time and space that the object comes into our existence.

The Atom and Light Spectrum Analysis

One might ask, "How do we know that matter is made up of frequencies?" This is proved using light spectrum analysis. It is known that each element in the universe has its own distinct spectral lines, which identify it. Spectral lines are different light wavelengths that the element produces when it is raised to a high potential. The light frequencies are a function of the information that make up the element, which gets you to the next question: What is light? That will be covered later. A prism de-modulates the light into its individual wavelengths. The process is called dispersion. What I believe we are looking at is a highly sophisticated form of pulse modulation (Figure 33); not only are these pulses amplitude-modulated, but they are frequency-modulated. For instance, the individual pulses are different colors and intensities. This would constitute the amplitude modulation part of the pulse modulation. The spaces between the pulses make up the frequency- or phase-modulated part of the pulse modulation. There may be other information superimposed on each individual pulse.

Is Light Particles or Wave Forms?

We have all marveled at the spectrum of color produced by a prism or a rainbow. We have all turned on light bulbs that produced every color imaginable. Even scientists still wonder what light really is, but so far it has defied understanding. Is it a particle, like Newton and quantum mechanics envisioned, or is it an electromagnetic wave as theorized by Maxwell?

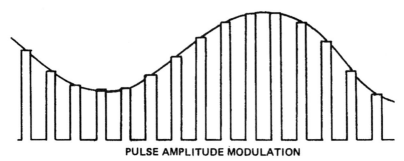

PULSE AMPLITUDE MODULATION

Figure 33: An example of pulse amplitude modulation

Quantum Mechanics Viewpoint

Max Planck first developed the theory of quantum mechanics in 1900. Later contributors included Albert Einstein. Planck was trying to find what the energy distribution of light emitted from a heated object was. He concluded from his experiments that the energy emitted could only be radiated in bundles of energy which he called quantums (Einstein later called these bundles photons). Planck calculated that these quantums of energy all had the same energy level (Planck's constant is $h = 6.626$ x 10^{-27} erg. sec.) times the frequency of radiation. Planck's conclusion was that solid matter can only radiate quantums of energy in the form of light.

Einstein added to Planck's conclusion by trying to explain the photoelectric effect. This is when electrons are produced from a metal when light strikes it. It was found through experimentation that the intensity of light has little to do with the velocity of the electrons "produced," but instead it was in direct proportion to the frequency of the light. In summary, Einstein-Planck's theory considers light as particles called photons, each photon having a certain amount of energy depending on its frequency (color). The momentum of each photon is equal to Planck's constant times the frequency, divided by the speed of light ($h \times f/c$).

The quantum theory is not considered perfect because, it cannot explain the phenomenon of interference lines and diffraction spectrum formed by a prism. Maxwell's electromagnetic theory of light was able to explain those phenomena, but could not explain the photoelectric effect.

Multidimensional Reality Explanation

Light is the demodulated information of an element passing by us at the speed of approximately 2.997925×10^8 meters per second. This speed is the rate at which the Diehold processes and transmits the information into our universe. Using the videotape analogy, the speed of light reflects the velocity the information passes over the head device. In other words, it is the speed of the tape recorder. Since the matter world we live in, is the "thing" that is being propagated into existence at the speed of light, that means light is really "still" information on the "tape."

A simple analogy: let's imagine you are in a plane that is flying at 400 mph. You are looking out the back of the plane while it is releasing a contrail behind it. To your point of view the contrail cloud is traveling away from you at 400 mph and you look like you are standing still. The vantagepoint of someone on the ground shows the contrail speed to be zero and your plane to be 400 mph. The light is like the contrail falling behind us. The only difference is in our dimension the light or information leaves this dimension 360° around the object.

My explanation for the observations made by Max Planck and Albert Einstein is this. They are correct seeing small packets of energy, which they called photons. The reason for seeing these small packets of energy is because the information for the atom is "blinking" in and out of our existence at the frequency of the information and carrier wave that makes up that element. Remember the information that makes up the matter world appears to be digital in nature, so it would "blink" in and out of our. Planck's constant is the amount of energy created when you have the electromagnetic field, representing the information of the atom, collapsing as it crosses the x axis and creating an electrostatic field 90° out of phase from the collapsing magnetic field. For this reason light has both a wave-nature, as well as a particle- nature to it.

Size of Objects Approaching the Speed of Light

The following is relevant to understanding what is **not** causing the gravitational anomalies.

$$\text{Length of objects} = \ell_0 \cdot \sqrt{1 - \frac{v^2}{c^2}}$$

$$\text{Duration of time} = \frac{t}{\sqrt{1 - \frac{v^2}{c^2}}}$$

Figure 34: The Lorenz transfor-mations for size and time.

The Theory of Multidimensional Reality does not disagree with The Special Theory of Relativity, in regarding time slowing down and objects getting smaller, when they approach the speed of light. The formulas that show this relationship are the Lorenz transformations (Figure 34).

There are two approaches to explain this phenomena. I am going to use the tape analogy because you can visually see it in Figure 35. Remember that the information on the tape is going past the head device at the speed of light, transmitting the information of all existence. Also, notice that it is impossible to go faster than the speed of light, because that's the speed you are propagated into existence. Also, you cannot go ahead in time because you cannot go beyond the head device or CPU that creates your existence, because you don't exist yet in the future. In Figure 35, at position 1 is Object "A" at rest, in our dimension, at a moment in time. Position 2 is some time in the future, but Object A (now identified as A') is now traveling at a speed of 100 million meters per second. Its size has reduced to 94.27% of its rest state, and time is now 1.0607 times longer.

The conclusion we must come to is that if we increase our velocity in the fourth dimension, and if we accept the idea that we cannot go faster than the Diehold creates our existence, then the result of our increased speed must be the stretching-out of Object A' information. To clarify this idea, let's go to Figure 35. We see that the area of the domains of information for Object A' has been stretched behind the present; therefore, having a greater equivalent mass. The shaded area in the diagram represents the greater domain of information. Because of its increased velocity, it also has an equivalent potential from its momentum. The reason why time slows down is because as Object A' approaches the speed of light, it is getting closer to the first

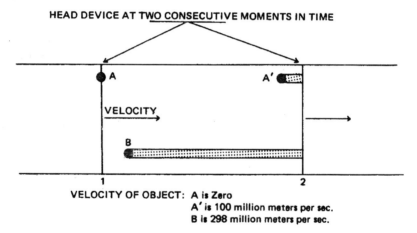

HEAD DEVICE AT TWO CONSECUTIVE MOMENTS IN TIME

VELOCITY OF OBJECT: A is Zero
A' is 100 million meters per sec.
B is 298 million meters per sec.

Figure 35: Velocity of object in our dimension; object "A" is zero; A' is 100 million meters per sec.; object B is 298 million meters per sec. Demonstrating the effects of velocity in the Diehold.

dimension where time has no meaning. Time is stopped in the storage dimension.

At position 2, the velocity of B is 298 million meters per second. The result would be that the information for Object B would be stretched to 917% behind its resting modulation point. This would be indicated by the fact that a clock placed on Object B would measure time 9.17 times slower than at rest. The mass of Object B would be 917% greater than at rest because

Object B is occupying a much larger domain of information on the tape. The increased field (information) would, in turn, reduce the size of B to only 10.9% of its original volume. This process would continue until the object reaches just under the speed of light. The result of this fantastic speed is that the object is becoming a first-dimensional object. It is returning to the information that made it up, where time is irrelevant. To get Object B to this fantastic velocity, it would take an equally fantastic amount of energy. Therefore, this method of transportation is highly inefficient and wasteful. We could more easily raise the potential of the object high enough and move the object in time and space using the Diehold instead of going against it.

Time

Time is relative to the dimension you are in. In the first and second dimension, time does not mean anything. In the rest of the dimensions, it means something. If you look at Figure 35, you will come to the conclusion that time is the result of the constant rate that information is "played out" from the Diehold. The third dimension is the inanimate world of matter and time definitely has meaning. The life forms of the fourth, fifth, and sixth dimensions are linear beings. That means they and we live and perceive reality over time. For all the life forms, the theory holds that none of them could go ahead in time, because they can't go beyond the CPU or "head device" that creates their existence.

The Natural Log

The natural log (*e*) shows up in everything! It is a transcendental number that is used as the base of natural logarithms. It is represented by the infinite series

$$e = 1 + \frac{1}{1!} + \frac{1}{2!} + \frac{1}{3!} + \frac{1}{4!} + \ldots + \frac{1}{n!} + \ldots$$

The numerical value for e = 2.71828 (approximately).

The natural logarithm, e^x grows faster than any power of x, as x→∞. Similarly, e^{-x} decays faster than any power of x^{-1} as x→∞. This rapid exponential growth and decay is observed in all physical, chemical, electrical, biological, and nuclear reactions. Radioactive elements will decay exponentially over time. Unchecked population growth tends to increase exponentially over time.

I have not found a philosopher or scientist yet who has explained why e shows up in our existence. It is one of the most important numbers in science and no one knows why it exists.

First you must ask; when is e showing up? The answer is, when something is building up or decaying. The Multidimensional Reality explanation is; the natural log shows up as a result of information being processed and entering our dimension. In the Basic Theory Section, I said "an object exists in three different dimensions almost at the same time." In the computer model of the universe, it describes information in a storage dimension, a transmission dimension, and as created matter. It also says that there is no time in the Diehold; and the transmission dimension (second dimension) is instantaneous. So where is the delay? It is in the CPU of the Diehold. Remember the Diehold is made by God, but it is also made up of matter. We don't see it because it's in another time-space relationship. Remember the observation of light dispersion and refraction. The light slows down when it enters the prism. Since the CPU is made of matter, as the information passes through it and gets processed, it slows down. This is why e shows up, it is a function of how the information is processed and transmitted into our existence.

On a personal level there is a phenomenon that you can relate to and understand how it manifests itself. All humans have experienced déjà vu multiple times in our life. To define it, so we all know what I'm talking about, déjà vu is when you are looking at some event and all of a sudden you think you dreamt that same exact event. Usually the event lasts for less than half a second. No action, on your part, can change the outcome of the event—it just happens. Our usual reaction and response is that we must have dreamt the event and had not recalled the dream until now.

If our existence emanates really from the Diehold, in another dimension, then our thinking process is also occurring there. The matter part of our brain is like a receiver for this information. What is happening with déjà vu is the information that makes up what we are doing and seeing is perceived twice. The first signal perceived directly from the Diehold, the second signal coming through our physical brain. It is like audio feedback. The signal is sent through the circuit twice. I don't know why this phenomenon happens or why some people have it more often than others do. This delay in the signal is an example of e , the natural log.

Isotopes and Error in the Universe

One might conclude from my theory that the only elements that would appear would be only one atomic weight per element. For instance, all the hydrogen found in our dimension would have an atomic weight of one or all carbon found would have an atomic weight of 12. What is known today, is that all elements have radioactive isotopes.

The definition of an isotope is an atom of the same element having the same atomic number, but a different atomic weight. The isotope is identical in all physical and all chemical properties. The only difference between them is their atomic weight.

Let's take the example of nickel. The vast majority of nickel found has an atomic weight of 58.7. Why would we find a small percentage of nickel having atomic weights of 59 and 63 and still be nickel? With an atomic weight of 63, it should be copper; but why is it still nickel? I don't know if anyone has ever thought about the phenomenon or wondered why it occurs. The only way I can explain the occurrence of isotopes is by using an information theory of existence.

Let's assume the Diehold is transmitting the information for nickel. The information consists of a variety of frequencies. The big question is how does the Diehold know that it is always transmitting the information for nickel at the correct frequencies? The way it would be done is the same method that is used in radio and television transmitters. The device is called a *phase detection circuit*. The circuit insures that the transmitter is producing the correct frequencies. It does this by comparing the correct frequency with any higher or lower frequency produced by the circuit. If the frequencies produced go too high, the phase detector senses it and corrects it by lowering the transmitted frequency. The same thing occurs if the transmitter frequency goes below its acceptable parameters.

The profound point to be made here is that—without the error, the transmitter does not know if it is producing the correct frequencies. I think the same principle holds true for the

Diehold. Ninety-eight percent of the signal information is transmitted at correct frequencies, which, in turn, modulates into the correct atomic weight for an element. The isotopes are the error factor found in our dimension. If this principle holds true for our universe, then we should see this error factor show up in everything from childbirth's, to plant seeds—a certain percent of these life forms will have natural defects.

Quasars

Energy levels from quasars are greater than can be explained from traditional physics. Quasars, which give off huge amounts of energy, 10^{58} ergs, which is the equivalent to consuming 500 million of our suns per second to produce the energies emitted throughout the electromagnetic spectrum.[3] A good summary of the problem traditional astrophysics is facing is found in the following quote from the astronomer, Dr. George Abell:

> "We have then the perplexing picture of a quasar: an extremely luminous object of small size displaying enormous changes in energy output over intervals of months or less from regions less than a few light months across; 100 times the luminosity of our entire galaxy is released from a volume more than 10^{17} times smaller than the galaxy."[4]

Thus, energy does not come from matter and so $E=mc^2$ is wrong. As Nikola Tesla said: "Nuclear energy is an illusion." The reason why it's incorrect is simple and blatant: if our galaxy, like all galaxies, went through the quasar stage of evolution some 15 billion years ago and had consumed matter for energy to produce the power quantities mentioned above, our quasar would have had to use up all its matter (certainly all of its hydrogen and helium) billions of years ago. To put it in simpler terms, this galaxy shouldn't exist today.

My explanation is, quasars can be analogized to transient or bias voltages produced on the tape head of a recording device. The bias voltages on the head device far exceed the voltages produced by the domains of the tape passing over the head. If any of these voltages should leak through to the tape, more energy would seem to appear available from the tape system than exists on the entire tape.

Kirlian Photography and the Phantom Leaf Effect

Not too often can an experimental piece of equipment, costing less than $100 in parts, prove a theory with one phenomenon. The phantom leaf effect, produced by Kirlian photography, is a phenomenon caused by passing a high voltage at a high frequency (ranging from 3,000 hertz to 5 MHz) through a leaf with a photographic plate on one side. It is not really photography using cameras or even lenses. It is a high voltage, high frequency effect. The electron discharge is what exposes the photographic film. Figure 36 shows a cross section of how a unit is set up.

The phantom leaf effect is produced when 2% to 10% of a leaf is cut away and placed between the plates. When the leaf is properly "photographed" with the correct frequency, the cutaway section of the leaf will appear as if it is still there. It looks like small bubbles and light streamers, coming from the area that is no longer there. The resulting light pattern outlines the superstructure of the leaf. It is not often that this phantom appears. Figures 37 and 38 show two leaves that have been cut off and photographed in such a manner. Figure 37 shows the right side of the leaf cut off. The small bubbles of light outline the former shape of the leaf. Figure 38 shows the top of the leaf cut off. Only light streamers outlining the former leaf shape is visible.

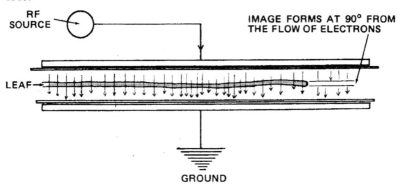

Figure 36: Cross section of a Kirlian "photographic" unit where the object would be placed.

Some experimenters have reported a 5% success rate in getting phantoms. The phantom images are not a residue from the leaf before it was cut off. The first time it ever came into contact with the film is after it is cut. The leaf is then photographed and the phantom appeared. This experiment was done many times to show it is a repeatable phenomenon. No one has understood why this could happen or even thought of the consequences of what it means if the phantom leaf is true and is a repeatable experiment.

Multidimensional Reality Explanation

First you must ask yourself, "How does a leaf know how to recreate its original image?" If you consider what the leaf has

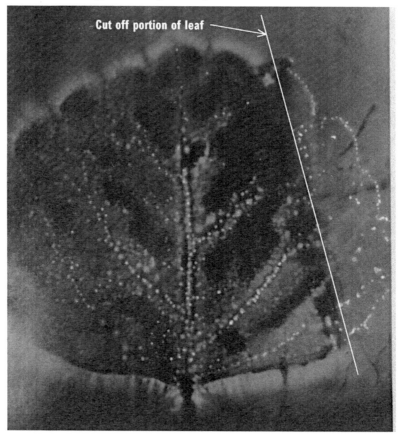

Figure 37: Phantom leaf effect from a cut leaf. Courtesy of T. Moss, UCLA

going for it, in this dimension, the answer is: it doesn't know how to reconstruct its original shape. The only possible answer for the appearance of the phantom effect is that the information for the whole leaf exists in another dimension. The life and conscious energy part of its information exists in another dimension. Since the only way to make this phantom appear is by using a high voltage, high frequency device, this implies that the

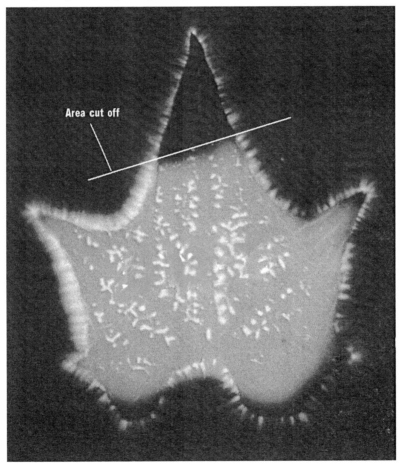

Area cut off

Figure 38: Phantom leaf effect from a cut leaf. Courtesy of Hernani Andrade, Brazilian Institute of Psychobiophysical Investigation.

signal that makes up the leaf is a modulated signal of some sort. Otherwise, we couldn't possibly have made the image appear. As we look at the phantom portion of the leaf, we notice that the bubbles of light and the aura around the edges are quite visible. The only thing that isn't present is the light that makes up the actual matter in this dimension. Part of the signal that we are looking at is the carrier wave, the clocking and synchronizing frequencies that make up that portion of the leaf, along with the conscious energy that is the "soul" of the plant. The pulsations observed from the phantom are the result of these different frequencies.

The phantom leaf effect also proves, very simply, that energy does not come from matter ($E = mc^2$). In the two pictures we are seeing energy not being emitted from matter; it is just a field produced by a domain of information.

Chapter Conclusion

In this chapter I have tried to explain The Theory of Multidimensional Reality. It is a very abstract idea, but I hope the few analogies that were given helped you understand it. If you desire a complete version of Chapter six, that can be found in my book, *Secrets of the Universe* (161 pages). The cost is $13.95 (postage included) and if you want to receive the complete Excel® spread sheets for all of the tables and charts mentioned in that book, they can be acquired by sending $7.00 to Vector Associates, PO Box 40135, Bellevue, WA 98015.

[1]Plato, The Sophist, Vol. 7, pp. 371, Loeb Classical Library, Harvard University Press, 1967.
[2]I am taking liberties with the word modulation because the traditional meaning of modulation is the process of impressing information in the form of a frequency onto a carrier wave frequency, at high-power, if the modulator is directly connected to a load. In this case the "modulation point" means entry point into our existence.
[3]G. Setti, (ed.), Structure and Evolution of the Galaxies, (Holland, D. Reidel Publ., 1975).
[4]G. O. Abell, Exploration of the Universe, 3ed. ed. (Holt, Rinehart & Winston, N.Y., 1975).

Chapter 7

Conclusion

Answers to Gravitational Anomalies

Time and Size Changes

The most obvious attraction in these gravitational anomalies, is the size change. The time changes are a new discovery due to my experiments. The two phenomena are related but not in the same ratio that the Lorenz transformations call for. With size changes of 5.8% we should be seeing time being effected much more then we do. If these vortexes were formed by "natural" formations then maybe traditional equations would produce better results. The other interpretation could be that the actual time-size relationship will not be approximated using the traditional gravitation equations and that traditional physics does not know what gravity or time is. I contend the truth will prove to be the latter. In Chapter 6 time was explained as a result of the rate of information processed, through the Diehold, that make up our reality. Since the speed of the information through the "CPU" is constant therefore time and size stays constant. The only problem I see is that the experiments found that time shifted up and sometimes down. The General Theory of Relativity says it should only slow down. Why is it shifting up? We know the size percentage changes during the day and from day-to-day. The

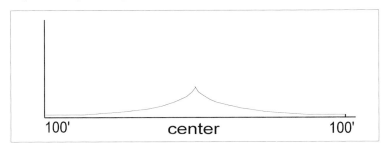

Figure 39: Graph depicting the information density towards the center of a gravitational vortex.

only set of circumstances that can explain these observations is something is able to dynamically change the rate (time) at which information is modulated into our existence and also independently control information density (size).

Why do Some Trees Grow Leaning Clockwise Inside the Vortex

Gibberellins are plant hormones which tell a plant which way is up. Of course "up" normally is away from the earth. But inside these gravitational vortices the plant is being fooled because gibberellins really sense which direction information is coming from. Inside these vortices information must be spiraling down like a cork-screw in a counter-clockwise direction. The plant senses the direction of the information coming at it and grows against it in a clockwise direction.

The reason some trees exhibit counter-clockwise twisted trunks is because I think they must be located on nodes inside the vortex. The growth rate of the tree itself has a differential causing the twisted tree trunk.

Moving a Dead Weight Towards the Center of the Vortex

The reason it takes more force to push a dead weight towards the center of a gravitational vortex than away is because you are crossing more lines of information. If you were to plot the density or amount of information per square foot it would plot like what is shown in Figure 39. Information is being compressed towards the center of the vortex. The center of the vortex is represented where the point is. The same effect is felt when you walk towards the center compared to away.

Physiological Effects of a Gravitational Vortex

Headaches is one common effect reported inside these vortexes. The reason for this effect, has to do with your eyes and the time differential inside the vortex. The distance between your two eyes is about 2.5 to 3 inches. Your brain takes these two electrical signals and processes them by combining signals and making one image. There is a very slight time differential between these two signals inside the vortex. The brain tries to synchronize them and generally succeeds but in the process some people get headaches because the brain must work harder. Headaches may also develop due to signal and timing differentials within your brain.

The Jell-O Effect

This was a real puzzling phenomenon inside the vortex. What was happening was the frequency counter was recording wide swings in frequencies when the crystal was first introduced into the vortex. The phenomenon happened at all three locations. After some time the frequency counter began to record more stable frequencies. I am sure about what was going on after my third trip to the Oregon Vortex.

On the third trip, on June 9, I was recording the frequency at one location inside the vortex, for a long period of time. I had a clear view of the whole vortex, and who was in it and who wasn't. Sometimes I noticed swings of 15 hertz over a short period of time. Sometimes the frequency was very stable. I correlated that the frequency was most stable when no one was in the vortex. Once I watched as five young people walked into the vortex and the frequency counter responded with a frequency fluctuation of 10+ hertz.

Conclusion

Are these gravitational anomalies caused by a large chunk of metal, such as a meteor, buried in the earth below? Absolutely not! The area of the vortex is too well defined in a small area, and the size of objects as well as time is changing over time (see video tape analogy). For a normal gravitational body to do this, it would mean that its mass would have to be changing dynamically and that is impossible. If it was caused by such a huge mass of iron or other dense metal, then we would be observing a huge meteor creator like the one in Arizona and we are not. Finally the gravitational field seems to be interacting with people and frequency generating devices that enter it. Size and time seem to be changing independently. So if this effect is not caused by "natural" forces then what could cause it?

Remember my explanation of what gravity is, namely that it is concentrations of information directed to a point in time and space. What I think is causing these vortices is a computer-like device built by a highly advanced civilization, that lived on the planet a long time ago. Maybe it was the "Golden race of beings" mentioned in many mythologies. What is interesting is that it seems these devices are still working and have the capacity to sense human presence by adjusting its field. Maybe if one is dug up we will know for sure?